POSTCA from PALESTINE

Andrew Reid

St Matthias Press

© Andrew Reid, 1989

Published by
St Matthias Press
PO Box 225
Kingsford NSW 2032

Scripture taken from the HOLY BIBLE, NEW INTER-NATIONAL VERSION. Copyright © 1973, 1978, 1984 International Bible Society. Used by permission of Zondervan Publishers.

ISBN 1 875245 04 9

Contents

Introduction

This guide has been written with a number of factors in mind, each of which I have experienced both in my ministry amongst university and college students, and in Christian circles generally.

Firstly, there is a significant disparity between many students' grasp of their own discipline and their grasp of Christian truth. Many Christian students are Biblically illiterate. Most don't read the Bible and many don't even know where to start in reading the Bible and systematically interpreting it for themselves.

Secondly, there is a lot of childish Biblical interpretation amongst Christians, students and otherwise. Often this is not their own fault, but the result of bad modelling in their churches and Christian groups.

Thirdly, Australian Christians are becoming satisfied with being passive 'pew sitters', continually being told by 'experts' what the Bible says. Increasingly, Biblical interpretation is being placed in the hands of a select group of 'priests' who communicate the truth to the rest of us. Even though Bibles are now within the grasp of the everyday person, we have stopped reading and interpreting for ourselves. If this continues, the health of Christianity in Australia is very much under threat.

I am convinced that the Bible is an open book for all. It is not for a special brand of people with inside knowledge. It is for *us*. We have minds and we have God's Spirit. We

1

can be our own Biblical interpreters.

While recognizing this basic fact, this guide is written with a further conviction—that the Bible is not simplistic. Diligent and concentrated work is needed if we are to fathom the riches and wonders to be found in God's word.

Lastly, having read widely on Biblical interpretation, I am further convinced that there is a desperate need for a 'hands on' approach to teaching Christians how to interpret the Bible. We don't so much need someone to tell us 'how to do it', but someone to:

- tell us the how to's
- demonstrate those how to's in action
- get us to actually do it in a structured situation.

This conviction explains the format of this guide. Most of the units contain a principle of Biblical interpretation and some information on what it means. This is followed by some examples of the principle being applied ('Examples'). The third section ('Hands on') gives some exercises which apply the particular principle. The 'Hands on' sections work through the book of Haggai.

How to use this guide

Although individuals can certainly use this guide on their own, it is designed to be done under the supervision of someone skilled in Biblical interpretation (eg. an AFES Staffworker or church leader). If you intend working through the material in a group or course, we suggest that you have 13 sessions of 1-1½ hours, using a program like the one on the next page.

Before each session (except Session 1) each member reads the material for the coming session and works through the 'hands on' exercises. Wide margins have been left for you to jot down notes, questions and comments throughout the text. You will also notice that Bible verses mentioned in the text which have an asterisk (*) after them are printed in the margins. Write your answers to the 'hands on' material in this guide—this is a book to be written on.

When the group gets together, discuss your notes and questions from the text and the Examples, and compare answers for the 'hands on' material.

The distinctive thing about this guide is its hands on

Suggested program for small groups

SESSION	MATERIAL IN GUIDE	
1	Read this INTRODUCTION together	
2	OVERVIEW	
3	STEP 1	DEPEND ON GOD FOR ENLIGHTENMENT
	STEP 2	DETERMINE THE AUTHOR'S INTENTION
	2.1	Get acquainted
4	2.2	Literary type
5	2.3	Structure
6	2.4	Meaning
7	2.5	Geography
8	2.6	History
9	2.7	Context
10	2.8	Summing up
11	STEP 3	DETERMINE OTHER MEANINGS
	3.1	Links with other parts of the Bible
12	3.2	Biblical context
13	STEP 4	DETERMINE THE SIGNIFICANCE FOR ME

approach, and I cannot stress too strongly the importance of doing the 'hands on' material. Breaking the bad reading habits of a Christian life-time is not done easily or quickly. Put in the work now, and reap the benefits for years to come.

Before we get down to work, I'd like to answer an important preliminary question, and clear a space for us to work in.

Why bother with the Bible?

The Bible is a definitive book, a book that gives definitive answers to the sorts of questions we all ask at some point in our lives.

- What is human life all about?
- Why is man's story such a puzzling combination of achievement and failure, goodness and badness, success and degradation?
- Where is the world going?

3

■ Is there a God?
■ What is God like?
■ Can we relate to God?
■ On what basis can we relate to God?
■ Is life worth living?
■ What sort of life ought we to live?
■ Are there any standards we should be living up to?
■ How is it possible to live up to them?

> *The Bible is intended to be (and can be) understood even by the most simple person because its essential content is clear and easily understood.*

Rather than giving us packaged answers, the Bible deals with these great questions by telling us the story of God's dealings with his creation in general and with man in particular, and by making some clear (and not so clear!) statements about what God thinks about them.

But the Bible is not only important because it answers the questions we all ask. It is important because, as it tells stories and makes statements, it answers the questions that *God* thinks need answering. It does this most clearly when it reaches the climax of God's story of his dealings with men: the story of Jesus Christ.

With the coming of Jesus and his death and resurrection, relationship between God and man is made possible. In Jesus it is possible to enjoy that relationship with God which God had intended from the beginning.

This is why we bother with the Bible—it tells us about Jesus, about God and about how to live in relationship with God. In the words of Paul, we bother with the Bible because its writings are "able to instruct you for salvation through faith in Christ Jesus" (2 Timothy 3:15).

Clearing the Ground

Before getting into the mechanics of interpreting the Bible it is important to clear a bit of ground on which we can work. We can do this by making some positive statements and by looking critically at some misconceptions which we have about the Bible.

The Bible:
A book that everyone can read

The first point we need to bear in mind as we read the Bible is that it is 'perspicuous' or clear and lucid. The Bible is intended to be (and can be) understood even by the most simple person because its essential content is clear and easily understood.

Practically, this means that Christians believe:

- that the Bible (and Christianity) is not about mysterious, hidden things that require some special sort of insight or initiation to understand; and
- that the Bible does not need some special caste of people to unravel it. The Bible is for all and is understandable by all. If you have an open Bible and a sound mind, then you are equally able to come to conclusions about what God is saying as the 'great ones'.

The Bible: A book that needs hard work

While the Bible is 'perspicuous' and able to be understood by the most simple person this does not mean that it is a simple book. It is a book from God, who is not simple, whose thoughts are far above our thoughts, whose wisdom and knowledge are deep and rich, whose judgments are unsearchable and whose ways are inscrutable (see Romans 11:33-36*).

Therefore, although almost anyone can understand the Bible, understanding the whole Bible and learning of the God who stands behind it will be a lifelong task requiring all that we have to give it.

The mention of 'hard work' and 'a lifelong task' gives us trouble. Being the sinful people that we are, we want easy ways out. We want a surefire, time-saving way of reading the Bible that will guarantee results. Here are some of the more frequently heard excuses for avoiding serious study of the Bible.

 Oh, the depth of the riches of the wisdom and knowledge of God!
How unsearchable his judgments, and his paths beyond tracing out!
"Who has known the mind of the Lord? Or who has been his counselor?"
"Who has ever given to God, that God should repay him?"
Romans 11:33-35

'The Bible is self explanatory and self interpreting'

By this, people mean that you don't need anything else to understand the Bible—there is no need for outside help of any sort.

Of course there is a real element of truth to this proposition. The Bible *is* perspicuous. It can be understood without aid by anyone who can read.

However, there is also some erroneous thinking here. The error can be seen even at the most basic level: the Bible is written in Hebrew, Aramaic and Greek. Most of us do not have access to any of these languages. And even if we did, these languages cannot be understood without reference to the culture in which they were developed. Therefore, in the very act of using an English translation, we are dependent on outside knowledge (in the shape of other documents which help us determine the meaning of the original languages).

At another level, some parts of the Bible are quite difficult to understand without bringing in outside material. A good example of this is Mark 13:14*.

Notice that the writer inserts an editorial comment in the speech of Jesus urging the reader to understand, presumably by bringing in outside data, either from previous literature (eg. the book of Daniel) or from past or contemporary incidents.

> *When you see 'the abomination that causes desolation' standing where it does not belong—let the reader understand—then let those who are in Judea flee to the mountains.*
>
> Mark 13:14

'I just pray and the Holy Spirit tells me what it means'

This is a common mistake in approaching Scripture. It is really a form of the error immediately above.

1 Timothy 4 is a helpful antidote, along with other references throughout 1 and 2 Timothy and Titus. These passages stress the need for diligence, faithfulness, seriousness and right handling of the truth in our study of Scripture.

As well as these encouragements in Scripture, closer examination reveals that this way of thinking doesn't stand up. Suppose for a moment that things really happened this way, and that merely by praying and glancing at the Bible we could come to know what it means. If we pursue this to its logical conclusion, we must say that *God* has given me this meaning and that therefore it cannot be questioned (and must be true for everyone!). We end up with multitudes of 'Spirit-inspired interpreters' and with no gauge by which to test them. The value of the Bible as an authoritative, God-breathed reference point is reduced to practically nothing. How will we ever know the truth?

'The mind is a bad thing'

There is an underlying suspicion amongst Christians today about the mind. Expressions such as that given above ('I just pray and the Holy Spirit tells me what it means') demonstrate that suspicion. We are in an anti-intellectual period of Christianity. There are numerous reasons for this. We are cynical about 'professional' theologians and Biblical scholars, who seem to compromise their belief in the truth for the sake of academic respectability. We feel swamped by the prejudice and ridicule of the world, and are often outgunned in technical and philosophical learning. We have a deep-rooted fear that Christianity will not stand the test of intellectual scrutiny.

Thus, it is common to find a massive disparity between tertiary students' grasp of their own discipline and their grasp of the Bible. I have encountered graduates who have risen to the top of their particular discipline and can answer almost any question about it, but at the same time have not risen above a most rudimentary (if not primary school) understanding of Scripture.

We cannot succumb to this and retreat into the bunkers of subjectivity. The Bible is addressed primarily (though not exclusively) to our *understanding*. It concerns our minds. Christianity is supremely intellectual; it is rational. What is more, the Bible will be able to stand the onslaught of man's intellectual examination if God is really behind it!

A practical guideline I have often used in ministering to students is that if they are to read the Bible intelligently they should read it in proportion to their general education. This would mean, for example, that students should spend at least as much time and effort studying the Bible as they would studying one subject at university (at a similar or greater depth!).

> *The Bible is addressed primarily (though not exclusively) to our understanding. It concerns our minds.*

The Guru syndrome

Throughout its history, Christianity has had problems with the fact that we, as human beings, prefer the exciting to the mundane, and the experiential to the rational. This is reflected in how we judge those who speak the Gospel to us. We tend to judge speakers on whether or not they are 'exciting' or 'spiritual'. Many of us push this even further by making such people 'gurus'. Swayed by their impressiveness, we depend upon them rather than upon God, the Holy Spirit, the Scriptures, or our own minds. To hear the following is not unusual:

"It's great going to my church and hearing our minister. The greatest thing about it is that if I ever have a problem with the Bible, I only have to go to the tape library at church. I know he will have spoken on it, and will have given an answer to my question. And most likely, he will be right."

We don't have to restrict such comments to speakers. We can do the same with authors, publishers, and the like. At the theological college I attended, it was common for students to go first to the 'authoritative' commentators when preparing sermons because they didn't want to say anything wrong. The second port of call was the Bible. It was also common to go to the Bible first, prepare, then check out your conclusions with the 'authoritative' and 'right' commentators, and then amend your conclusions appropriately.

Again there is an element of truth that needs to be affirmed here. God has greatly blessed us with gifted and godly older Christians, teachers and preachers who have insight and wisdom. It is right to listen to them and consult with them. They have been given their gifts to equip us for ministry, to help us grow in godliness, and to keep us from being tossed back and forward by every wind of doctrine (Ephesians 4:11-14).

On the other hand, the Bible is clear in affirming that the mark of the new covenant is that each of us can know God ourselves and need not be dependent on people standing between us and God, acting as God for us (see Hebrews 8:8-12 which quotes Jeremiah 31:31-34; also see 1 John 2:18-27).

Further, we need to recognize that all gurus stand on feet of clay. They all stumble in what they say and they are not nearly as dependable as God, who reveals himself in the Scriptures and who gives us his Spirit (James 3:1-2*; also see Acts 20:25-33).

We could take a lesson from the Bereans in this regard. Upon hearing Paul preach, they went back to the authoritative Scriptures to test what he was saying (Acts 17:10-12).

Not many of you should presume to be teachers, my brothers, because you know that we who teach will be judged more strictly. We all stumble in many ways. If anyone is never at fault in what he says, he is a perfect man, able to keep his whole body in check.

James 3:1-2

Two Sorts of Bible Study

Topical

Topical Bible study is where a particular theme of the Bible (eg. righteousness, love, temptation, women in the church, salvation) is studied to see what the Bible as a whole has to say about it.

Expository

Expository Bible study is where particular passages are studied as they come to us from the author himself.

Of course, topical and expository Bible study are interlinked. Solid, systematic, expository Bible study is the groundwork for any topical study of the Bible. For this reason, it is fundamental that we get expository study sorted out first. Only when we work out what words, phrases and ideas mean in their original context are we ready to link them up with occurrences of the same words, phrases and ideas in other parts of the Bible.

Because of its foundational importance, expository Bible study is the focus of this guide. The skills you will acquire will be particularly useful for systematically studying smaller passages within a larger book of the Bible.

Overview

What is Interpretation? ▪

Interpretation is one of the most basic, unrecognized and spontaneous activities in our lives. Whenever we listen to someone else, open our mail, or look at the way someone acts, we engage in interpretation.

Because of this, the best way to approach the whole question is to examine what happens when a person communicates with someone else. As we understand this process, we will get some idea of how to receive that communication (ie. how to interpret).

Take this postcard I received not long ago:

Dear Andrew,
How are you and the family?
Joel and Daniel must be having a good holiday. How is AFES going? Won't be going to the conference and have written to Terry to let him know.
Still on hols and running out of things to do. Hope something interesting comes up soon!
Wish you all a Merry Christmas and wish Ken too!

Regards, Priscilla

11

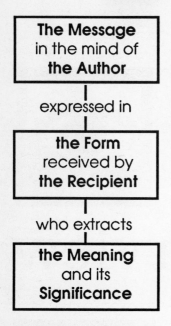

The Message
in the mind of
the Author

expressed in

the Form
received by
the Recipient

who extracts

the Meaning
and its
Significance

There are some fundamental (and obvious!) things to note about this communication. *Firstly,* there are two people involved:

■ the author
■ the recipient.

Secondly, there are three 'entities' involved in the process of communication:

■ the message the author wants to convey
■ the form of communication (in this case, a special kind of personal letter—the postcard)
■ the meaning or significance of the communication for the recipient.

Thirdly, of these three entities, there is only one which exists in tangible form—the form of communication (in this case, the text of the postcard).

This can be summed up in the simple diagram on the left.

Let us have a look at each of these in detail.

The Author

The author wants to get something across to a second person. For this to happen she needs to choose a way of saying it (in this case, writing), whilst making sure that the message is understandable and informs, commands or persuades in the way she intends.

From this it can be seen that communication and understanding are closely tied together and that interpretation involves placing ourselves in the author's situation to see what she was trying to say.

The Recipient

What about the recipient (me!)? The letter makes him ask himself, "What is this all about? What does this mean?".

In everyday communication this happens automatically. We don't stop to think about it. We just do it. We hear or read words, assess their meaning, and begin to formulate some response (a feeling, a determination to do something or not do something, and so on).

The Eavesdropper

There is, of course, a third party to this whole communication: the eavesdropper (you!). You stumble across

12

this communication at some time and place and ask, "What is this all about?" or "What is there in this for me?".

As we eavesdrop on this communication, we are in a similar situation to the real recipient. We, too, have to ask, "What is this saying? What does this mean?" We, too, have to interpret the communication, finding out what was being said (the meaning) and what difference that is going to make for us personally.

But we are at a disadvantage compared with the real recipient. We don't know the author personally. We don't know her situation nor the people she refers to, nor the recipient. Who are Joel, Daniel, Terry and Ken? Who, for that matter, is Andrew? What is AFES? We are not familiar with her unique ways of expressing herself or her temperament and personality. What, for example, are 'hols'?

Everyday Communication and Interpreting the Bible

Thinking about communication between people is a helpful way of thinking about interpreting the Bible. It raises questions that we need to think about and pitfalls that we need to avoid.

Similarities

Firstly, there are real similarities between interpreting the Bible and eavesdropping on someone else's correspondence. It is similar in the following ways:

■ When we read the Bible we are in fact 'eavesdropping'. There is a human author communicating to a recipient/s other than ourselves and we are a third party.

This gives us a basic ground rule for interpreting the Bible: What the Bible says to us will arise out of what the author intended to say to the original hearers.

In other words, when we interpret the Bible we are asking, "How does what the original author said to the original hearers relate to us?" We should not disregard the original context and readership and assume that it is written with us alone in mind.

■ The text is primary. It is the only thing which is tangible (and infallible).

13

This is very helpful when it comes to interpreting the Bible. It means that the Bible itself is the supreme authority. When any other thing comes into conflict with Scripture (eg. an individual, a theological system, the church, or our reason) then Scripture must take precedence.

■ Like my postcard, the Bible will be hard to understand if we don't don't know a bit about the people, situation, relationships, language and history of the author and readers. If our postcard had been written in Chinese then this point could have been emphasized by leaving it untranslated.

Differences

We need to realize that there are some differences between interpreting the Bible and eavesdropping on two way correspondence between parties other than ourselves.

For a start, some books of the Bible are written for more than one audience in more than one context (eg. Proverbs, Colossians).

Further, because we believe that the Bible has another author apart from the human one (ie. God) we believe three things, and these three things have corresponding dangers.

We believe that:

■ in some sense it was also written 'for us' (see Matthew 22:31-32, where Jesus quotes Exodus 3:6 to the Jews of first century Palestine).

■ there may be other meanings intended by God but not intended by the original author (1 Peter 1:10-13*, 2 Peter 1:19-21).

■ one piece of writing in the Bible does not stand on its own. It is part of a whole body of writing with the same divine author. There will be, therefore, various unifying strands running through it.

But we must be wary of:

✗ forgetting the real life situation in which Scripture arose and thinking that we can jump straight to the 'for us' meaning.

✗ throwing aside all restraint and reading things into Scripture that cannot be substantiated and that are totally foreign to the original meaning.

✗ working out 'the' unifying theme of the Bible and sifting every passage through it. It is easy for our theo-

Concerning this salvation, the prophets, who spoke of the grace that was to come to you, searched intently and with the greatest care, trying to find out the time and circumstances to which the Spirit of Christ in them was pointing when he predicted the sufferings of Christ and the glories that would follow. It was reavealed to them that they were not serving themselves but you, when they spoke of the things that have now been told you by those who have preached the gospel to you by the Holy Spirit sent from heaven. Even angels long to look into these things.
Therefore, prepare your minds for action; be self-controlled; set your hope fully on the grace to be given you when Jesus Christ is revealed.
1 Peter 1:10-13

14

logical systems to become too important and to blind us to what the text of Scripture is actually saying. Let's try to fit this all together.

The Bible: The Word of God

As Christians, we believe that the Bible is the word of God to man. By this we mean that:

■ the Bible is a book with a divine author that conveys timeless truths.

■ the Bible is 'God-breathed' (ie. 'inspired').

The implications of believing this are that we understand that:

➡ true Biblical interpretation must be done in dependence upon God for enlightenment. If we are to interpret the Bible accurately we must be in tune with the God who ultimately lies behind it. We must ask that God will be active in our minds, showing us what the passage means both for the original readers and for us. Our study of the Bible must be done in the context of prayer.

➡ the Bible will have implications for us today.

➡ we must stand under the Bible's authority. Studying the Bible is not merely an interesting academic exercise. It is listening to God speak. This means that we must not only depend on him for enlightenment, but also have receptive hearts and wills that are determined to obey what we hear.

➡ we may very well find that there are things in the Bible that the human author was unaware of saying but that God intended should be said.

➡ the Bible 'hangs together'.

➡ the text of Scripture is primary.

> ❛ *If we are to interpret the Bible accurately we must be in tune with the God who ultimately lies behind it.*

The Bible: The Human Side

As Christians, we believe that the Bible is also a human book in that it was written by human beings in human situations to other human beings in human situations. By this we mean that:

■ the Bible is a book with human authors that conveys timeless truths from God couched in human words.

■ the authors of the Bible were not mere robots or automatons who lent their hands and pens to God. On the contrary, when each author wrote, he had his own personality, his own history and his own way of expressing himself.

15

■ when each author wrote he did so as a human being of his age, with various preconceptions concerning the nature of man, the world and society. He wrote with the language and idiom of his surroundings to an audience who also held the various preconceptions of their age concerning the nature of man, the world and society.

The implications of believing this are that we understand that:

➡ what the Bible says to us will arise out of what the author intended to say to his original hearers.

➡ the Bible will be hard to understand fully if we know nothing of *the author*, his world, situation, history, personality and language.

➡ the Bible will be hard to understand fully if we know nothing of *the readers*, their world, situation, history, culture and language.

A Method for Interpreting the Bible

A method of interpreting the Bible that acknowledges this two-sided nature of the Bible is outlined on the following pages. Steps 1, 3 and 4 reflect the Bible's inspired and authoritative nature, while step 2 bears in mind its human character.

The four steps of the method, and the principles on which they are based, form the structure for the material that follows. We will work through the method together step by step, examining the principles, seeing them in action and actually using them ourselves.

As we do this, it is important that we realize the deficiencies and artificiality of such a way of interpreting the Bible.

Its structured approach is very different to the way that we normally interpret anything. However, given that most of us have learnt bad ways of interpreting the Bible, it is necessary to re-learn these basic skills in a structured way. The aim of the method is that eventually the process will become automatic and you will be able to throw away the 'four-step method'. (To help you remember the method, we have devised an 'icon' for each step.)

Further, some parts of the method are not applicable to our interpretation of particular passages in the Bible.

The passage we are studying will indicate this. For example, knowing the author, historical situation or items of geography may be totally unnecessary or impossible to determine in reading some of the wisdom books (ie. Psalms, Proverbs, Ecclesiastes). In our normal everyday interpretation of communication we learn to sift, to ask questions, and not to apply some questions. I trust that you will learn to do likewise with the Bible as you proceed.

Over the page is a brief outline of the method.

Finding a Time and Place

It should be immediately obvious that the type of Bible study we are talking about is not the sort of thing that is going to be easily squashed into a 20 minute daily 'Quiet Time'.

The best way forward is to continue reading the Bible the way you already do during your 'Quiet Time' and set aside a more substantial regular time that you can give to concentrated Bible study—for example, a two hour spot each Sunday afternoon when you can work hard at a particular passage or book of the Bible. Eventually the skills you learn here will become automatic and begin to rub off on your daily reading of the Bible.

Hands on

1

Read the four excerpts on pages 20-21 and answer the questions that begin on page 22.

THE METHOD

Step 1: Depend on God for enlightenment

Pray that God would be at work as you study his word, enlightening you and moving you towards faith in Christ and a life of obedience.

Step 2: Determine the author's intention

2.1 GETTING ACQUAINTED
Read through the book that you have chosen to study several times, noting its overall themes, and devising a brief outline of the contents.

2.2 LITERARY TYPE
Find out what type of literature you are dealing with.

2.3 STRUCTURE
See if there are any indications of an order or structural pattern intended by the author.

2.4 MEANING
Find out what all the words mean in...
- their immediate context
- the context of the book
- the context of the writer
- the context of its day
- the context of its Testament
- the context of the whole Bible (if a New Testament passage).

2.5 GEOGRAPHY
Ascertain whether the geographical setting is of importance to the meaning of the passage.

2.6 HISTORY
Find out whether the historical context is of importance to the meaning of the passage.
Ask these questions:
The AUTHOR:
 Who is he?
 What is his personal history?
 What is his situation?

The READERS:
>Who are they?
>What is their history?
>What is their situation?

CONTEMPORARY HISTORY:
>Are there any other current events at the time of writing which have relevance to the interpretation of the passage?

2.7 CONTEXT

Work out what place this passage plays in the thought of the surrounding passages and in the book as a whole.

2.8 SUMMING UP

Draw together what you have learnt from the passage as you used steps 2.1-2.7. This should yield the significance of this passage for its intended audience. Ask these questions:

What did this passage tell the original hearers about:

- God?
- the world?
- themselves and other people?
- the situations that they faced?

What feelings and/or actions do you think it may have been designed to evoke in their particular situation?

Step 3: Determine other Meanings

3.1 LINKS

See if there are other passages in the Bible that have direct *word, historical, theme* or *thought* links with this passage...

- within the Author's writings
- within the Testament
- within the Whole Bible.

3.2 BIBLICAL CONTEXT

Determine what place this passage has in the thought of the whole Bible.

Step 4: Determine the Significance for me

Sum up what you have learnt from the passage in STEPS 2 and 3, thus indicating the significance of the passage for its twentieth century audience. Ask these questions:

What does this passage tell *us* about:

- God?
- the world?
- ourselves and other people?
- the situations we face?

What feelings and/or actions should it evoke in my/our particular situation?

A

MOSCOW, Thursday: For the past two weeks, Moscow Hospital No 6, a nine-storey brown-brick building on the outskirts of the city, has been the centre of a desperate effort to treat the most seriously afflicted victims of the Chernobyl nuclear disaster.

Soviet and United States doctors and an Israeli specialist, using equipment and drugs airlifted from around the world, have raced around killing effects of radiation exposure in an attempt to save the lives of 33 men and two women who spent the first hours after the April 26 accident within metres of the damaged reactor.

One of the US physicians, Dr Robert Gale of the UCLA Medical Centre in Los Angeles, said that as of Wednesday evening seven of the 35 had died of radiation.

Dr Gale, 40, is chairman of the advisory committee of the international bone marrow transplant registry, a consortium of 128 transplant teams from 60 nations. The registry maintains computerised lists of more than 50,000 potential donors.

An intense, thin man with greying hair, he arrived in Moscow from the University of California on May 2 at the invitation of the Soviet Government.

His services had been offered by Armand Hammer, the American industrialist whose ties with Moscow date to 1921, when he was introduced to Lenin after helping combat a ty-phus epidemic in the Soviet Union.

Gale was joined several days later by Dr Richard Champlin and Dr Paul Terasaki of UCLA and Yair Reisner, a biophysicist from the Weizmann Institute of Science in Israel.

The Soviet authorities, disregarding the absence of diplomatic relations between their country and Israel and waiving normally stringent customs and immigration procedures, gave Reisner a visa when he landed at Moscow airport.

On Wednesday night, the Soviet leader, Mr Mikhail Gorbachev, said in a nationally televised address that the death toll had risen to nine—two killed in the original explosion and seven who have died since of radiation.

He said that as of today 299 people had been treated for radiation disease of varying degrees. That figure was 95 more than reported by Soviet officials last week.

In his TV speech, Mr Gorbachev noted the assistance of Gale and Terasaki and thanked the foreign 'business circles' that had provided equipment and medicines.

The Prime Minister, Mr Hawke, has written to Mr Gorbachev asking for his support for international measures to deal with nuclear accidents.

Dr Gale said that, based on his first-hand information and data provided by the Soviet health authorities, the total death toll from the accident, including one person killed by steam burns and another hit by falling debris, was now nine and would probably increase.

Hot Springs, January 30, 189-   **B**

Dear Pierrepont-

I knew right off that I had made a mistake when I opened the enclosed and saw that it was a bill for fifty-two dollars, 'for roses sent, as per orders, to Miss Mabel Dashkam'. I don't just place Miss Dashkam, but if she's the daughter of old Job Dashkam, on the open Board, I should say, on general principles, that she was a fine girl to let some other fellow marry. The last time I saw her, she inventoried about $10,000 as she stood—allowing that her diamonds would scratch glass—and that's more capital than any woman has a right to tie up on her back, I don't care how rich her father is. And Job's fortune is one of that brand which foots up to a million in the newspapers and leaves the heirs in debt to the lawyers who settle the estate.

C

Twas brillig, and the slithy toves
Did gyre and gimble in the wabe;
All mimsy were the borogoves,
And the mome raths outgrabe.

'Beware the Jabberwock, my son!
The jaws that bite, the claws that
   catch!
Beware the Jubjub bird, and shun
The frumious Bandersnatch!'

He took his vorpal sword in hand:
Long time the manxome foe he
   sought -
So rested he by the Tumtum tree,
And stood awile in thought.

And as in uffish thought he stood,
The Jabberwock, with eyes of flame,
Came whiffling through the tulgey
   wood,
And burbled as it came!

One, two! One, two! And through
   and through
The vorpal blade went snicker-snack!
He left it dead, and with its head
He went galumphing back.

'And hast thou slain the Jabberwock?
Come to my arms, my beamish boy!
O frabjous day! Callooh! Callay!'
He chortled in his joy.

Twas brillig, and the slithy toves
Did gyre and gimble in the wabe;
All mimsy were the borogoves,
And the mome raths outgrabe.

D

He thought his happiness was complete when, as he meandered aimlessly along, suddenly he stood by the edge of a full-fed river. Never in his life had he seen a river before—this sleek, sinuous, full-bodied animal, chasing and chuckling, gripping things with a gurgle and leaving them with a laugh, to fling itself on fresh playmates that shook themselves free, and were caught and held again. All was a-shake and a-shiver—glints and gleams and sparkles, rustle and swirl, chatter and bubble. The mole was bewitched, entranced, fascinated. By the side of the river he trotted as one trots, when very small, by the side of a man who holds one spellbound by exciting stories; and when tired at last, he sat on the bank, while the river still chattered on to him, a babbling procession of the best stories in the world, sent from the heart of the earth to be told at last to the insatiable sea.

Answer these questions about the four passages on pages 20-21.

(i)   Which of them convey the meaning by moods rather than by statement or propositions?

(ii)   Do you need to know details of the author, his/her background and his/her intent in writing to understand each of the excerpts?

(iii)   Do you need additional information other than that supplied within the excerpts to understand each of them?

(iv)   Since the skills of interpreting the Bible are essentially the same as those used for other literature, draw up a list of DOs and DON'Ts for good interpretation of any piece of writing.

DOs	DON'Ts
	eg. Don't look for hidden meanings without first trying to understand the general sense of the passage

(v)   If *first century readers* were reading these excerpts, what additional information would they need in order to understand each one?

A

B

C

D

2

What is the problem with the following interpretations, given what has been said in this overview:

(i)   In Isaiah 40:22 it says that God "sits enthroned above the circle of the earth". This is an indication that the earth was conceived of as being spherical by the writers of the Bible. (cf Isaiah 11:12; Jeremiah 49:36; Matthew 24:31; Revelation 20:7-8).

(ii)   In Luke 10:1-12 Jesus commands his disciples to preach the gospel. This is for us too. This passage tells us how we are to preach the gospel and outlines the characteristics that will mark true preachers of the gospel.

(iii)   Chapter 55 of Isaiah is God's promise that although I am going through a time of spiritual dryness at the moment it is not going to last. He is about to pour out his Spirit to bring new vitality and refreshment to my spiritual life.

(iv)   Although the Bible condemns sex outside marriage and also homosexuality, it only does so because it is reflecting the age and society in which it was written. The essence of the Bible is love and therefore it's quite okay to express our sexuality in this way today.

(v) I've been reading my Bible and praying, and this morning while I was praying God spoke to me and made it very clear that it was right for me to leave my wife and divorce her.

(vi) Jesus says that God's first commandment is that we love him and the second is that we should love our neighbour as we love ourselves. It is clear from this that God wants us to love ourselves. It is a commandment from him. The reason that so many of us can't love our neighbour is that we haven't learnt to love ourselves.

(vii) From Matthew 5:45 it is obvious that Jesus believed that the sun 'rises' and 'sets'. This is evidence that the earth is flat, or at least that it is the centre of the universe and that the sun revolves around the earth.

(viii) The book of Revelation is a book about the end of
the world. It's not much good me reading it—I'm
not part of the final generation of the world.

(ix) Chapter 11 of 1 Corinthians has nothing to say to
me today. It is a chapter totally concerned with a
first century situation that is irrelevant to us today.

STEP 1:

Depend on God for Enlightenment

Depend on God for Enlightenment

The Estate Agent bundled all four of us into his car. The day had finally come. We had lived frugally for seven years until we could put together a deposit. The bank had been through our finances with a fine toothcomb, stretched its rules, and finally given us a loan. All we needed was to find a house within our price range somewhere near the church we wanted to be part of.

Before getting into the car the Agent had shuffled through his endless lists looking for a suitable terrace house. As we drove around to look at them he kept talking to us, trying to find out what we really did need and whether he had anything that fitted the bill. He quizzed us about whether our limit really was our limit and whether there were any more children to cater for.

"You don't really need three bedrooms do you?" he asked. "There's only four of you. Two adults and two small children could easily fit into that two bedroom place I showed you, and it's in much better shape than the three bedroom ones I can offer."

Both Heather and I knew we needed the extra room, but it was our four-year-old son who best expressed our reasons as he chirped up from the back seat.

"No, we need three bedrooms—one for Mummy and Daddy, one for Joel and Daniel, and one for the books."

We chuckled to ourselves. There was a boy who knew his parents and their love of books.

I love books. I would gladly be shut up in a library for the rest of my life merely to read everything I could get my hands on. In my ideal world, I would be surrounded by things to read and by the ideas contained in them.

The Christian faith both feeds my love of books and blows it apart. On the one hand, Christianity is a religion that is concerned with books and therefore with my mind. It tells me that if I am to know God then I must acquaint myself with his self-revelation in Christ, which is spoken about in an inspired book.

On the other hand, Christianity goes far beyond the pages of the Bible and forces me out from my desk. It is a religion that is bound up with relating to living people—to God, to the world he has made and to the people he has made to live in it. The great and first commandment is not "Read a book about God and become acquainted with ideas about him" but "You shall love the Lord your God with all your heart, soul, strength and mind" and the second commandment is like it, "You shall love your neighbour as yourself". Reading the Bible may be the place where I get to know who God is, what he is like, what he has done for me and what he demands of me, but God intends that this knowledge should infiltrate my whole being, changing the way I relate to him and others.

Above all, you must understand that no prophecy of Scripture came about by the prophet's own interpretation. For prophecy never had its origin in the will of man, but men spoke from God as they were carried along by the Holy Spirit.

2 Peter 1:20-21

So right from the beginning we must make sure that God is involved in our interpretation of the Bible. It must not become an intellectual exercise divorced from him.

Even before we sit down to study the Bible, God has been involved. It was he who inspired the Bible writers through the Holy Spirit, so that as they wrote, they spoke from God (2 Peter 1:20-21* cf 1 Timothy 3:16). God, working through the human authors, is the divine author of Scripture.

And although we cannot have direct access to the human authors, we can have direct access to the divine author. If we are Christians, then we have the same Holy Spirit who inspired the passages we are reading. He knows what God wants us to understand from the Bible and, as we depend upon him, he will lead us into the truth and help us to obey it.

Before we start, then, we need to pray. We need to come before God, admitting our need for his help as we interpret and apply the passage. We need him to enlighten us, to show us how we need to change and to melt our resistance to do his will. We need to ask him to help us understand, remember, love and obey what we learn from the Scriptures so that we might live in a way that pleases him. The people who read the Bible this way are the ones whom God esteems (Isaiah 66:2*).

> *"This is the one I esteem: he who is humble and contrite in spirit, and trembles at my word."*
>
> *Isaiah 66:2b*

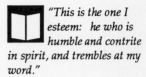

Examples

Here are some helpful models from Scripture and elsewhere that capture the right sorts of attitudes to reading the Bible.

Psalm 119:17-18

Do good to your servant, and I will live;
I will obey your word.
Open my eyes that I may see
wonderful things in your law.

Ephesians 1:17-19

I keep asking that the God of our Lord Jesus Christ, the glorious Father, may give you the Spirit of wisdom and revelation, so that you may know him better. I pray also that the eyes of your heart may be enlightened in order that you may know the hope to which he has called you, the riches of his glorious inheritance in the saints, and his incomparably great power for us who believe.

Philippians 1:9-11

And this is my prayer: that your love may abound more and more in knowledge and depth of insight, so that you may be able to discern what is best and may be pure and blameless until the day of Christ, filled with the fruit of righteousness that comes through Jesus Christ—to the glory and praise of God.

31

Blessed Lord, you have caused all holy scriptures to be written for our learning: grant us so to hear them, read, mark, learn, and inwardly digest them, that, encouraged and supported by your holy Word, we may embrace and always hold fast the joyful hope of everlasting life, which you have given us in our Saviour Jesus Christ.

(from *The Book of Common Prayer*)

Heavenly Father, give us faith to receive your word, understanding to know what it means, and the will to put it into practice; through Jesus Christ our Lord.

(from *The Book of Common Prayer*)

*

These sample prayers are not meant to give the impression that we just need to murmur a few words before we open our Bibles. Rather, the whole process of interpreting the Bible must be saturated with prayer. From beginning to end, we must read with God in mind. After we have finished our study, we should meditate on what we have learnt and ask God to help us see how we should change our attitudes and actions.

Hands on

If you haven't done so yet, stop, put down this book and spend some time praying about how you read the Bible. Pray about your attitudes, your current Bible reading practices (or lack of them!) and your desire to know God better. Ask him to open your mind to his word as you learn to study it more deeply using this guide.

Step 2:

Determine the Author's Intention

Step 2.1

Getting Acquainted

Before you even think about determining the author's meaning in a particular passage, there are a few basic things you must do. I have gathered these under the heading of Getting Acquainted.

Choose a book

Firstly, and most obviously, you need to pick a book of the Bible to study. To start with, choose one that is not too difficult or long (eg. a Psalm, Obadiah, Malachi, Galatians, 1 Peter, James). Later you can use the methods outlined here to look at larger books or parts of books.

In this guide, we will look at the short book of Haggai.

Get acquainted with the book

Before you start serious study of a passage or section, aim to read through the book you are going to study about four or five times.

1st time through: just read it from beginning to end without stopping.

2nd time through: read it again with pen in hand, noting things about the author (eg. his identity, his mood in writing, his situation, his whereabouts and details of his personality).

3rd time through: again with pen in hand, read through the book. This time note things about the recipients (eg. their identity, things implied about their character, things explicitly noted about them, their situation, whereabouts, needs, and condition at the time of writing).

4th time through: as you read through, jot down principal topics and dominant ideas taken up or addressed by the author.

Make up an outline of the book

Read the book again, this time making a provisional outline of the structure of the book. The aim here is to see how the author has laid out his material and how each part is related to the other. Don't forget that the original author didn't put in the chapter breaks, verse numbers or headings—all these have been added by people wanting to be 'helpful'.

For smaller books:

■ Look for major divisions (ie. notice breaks in thought, connecting words and changes in person). Give a title to each that clearly states the content of the section.

■ Look for natural subdivisions. Follow the same procedure as above, if possible making the title of the subdivision relate to the title of the major division.

For larger books:

■ Read the book paragraph by paragraph, giving a title to each (a word or phrase).

■ Combine the paragraphs into units, logically relating them in terms of thought, event, content or character, giving a title to each unit.

■ Combine units into sections, and sections into divisions following a similar procedure, again giving a title to each.

Consult a commentary or Bible dictionary.

Most commentaries or Bible dictionaries give an outline of the structure of a book. Compare yours with theirs. Don't automatically assume that they are right! Adjust your outline as you see fit.

You could have done this at the start and saved yourself a lot of trouble, but you would not have gained a feel for the book yourself, nor would you have read the Bible yourself (which is the purpose of this whole exercise)!

Take one of your divisions for detailed study

If you are studying the whole book then it is obviously best to start with the first of your sections (ie. about a chapter or so in length). If you are only wanting to study one section of a book (eg. Isaiah 53) then take that passage.

Now you are ready to get started on the detailed study of Scripture!

Examples

The following is a breakup of the book of 1 & 2 Samuel based on reading the book in the manner outlined above. It shows how a whole book can be broken up into sections, providing a helpful framework for understanding the whole book and manageable sections for detailed study.

1 Samuel 1.1-4.1a Samuel at Shiloh

1.1-8	Elkanah and his Family
1.9-21	Hannah's Prayer and God's Answer
1.21-28	Samuel's Dedication
2.1-11	Hannah's Hymn of Praise
2.12-36	Eli's Crooked Sons
3.1-18	God calls Samuel
3.19-4.1a	Samuel: God's Prophet

1 Samuel 4.1b-7.17 The Ark Narrative

4.1b-22	The Capture of the Ark
5.1-12	The Ark amongst the Philistines
6.1-7.2	The Return of the Ark to Israel
7.3-17	Samuel: God's Judge

1 Samuel 8.1-12.25 The Beginning of Israelite Kingship

8.1-22	Israel Asks for a King
9.1-10.16	Saul is Anointed by Samuel
10.17-27	Saul is Chosen and Proclaimed as King
11.1-15	Saul's Kingship is Confirmed
12.1-25	Samuel's Farewell Speech

1 Samuel 13.1-15.35 The Failure of Kingship under Saul

13.1-23	Saul is Rejected
14.1-52	Jonathan's Exploits
15.1-35	The War with the Amalekites

1 Samuel 16.1-2 Samuel 5.25 David's Rise to Power

16.1-13	The Anointing of David
16.14-23	At Saul's Court
17.1-58	The Slaying of Goliath
18.1-30	Relationships with the Saul's Family
19.1-24	Flight from Saul
20.1-42	Farewell to Jonathan
21.1-15	To Nob and Gath
22.1-23	Life as an Outlaw
23.1-29	Life in the Wilderness
24.1-22	Sparing Saul's Life (1)
25.1-44	Abigail
26.1-25	Sparing Saul's Life (2)
27.1-12	Life with the Philistines
28.1-25	The Witch of Endor
29.1-11	Rejected by the Philistines
30.1-31	War against the Amalekites
31.1-13	Saul's Death
2 Sam 1.1-16	The Report of Saul's Death
1.17-27	Lament for Saul and Jonathan
2.1-7	David is made King of Judah at Hebron

2.8-32	Civil War between David and Ishbosheth
3.1-39	The Murder of Abner
4.1-12	The End of Ishbosheth
5.1-16	David is made King of all Israel in Jerusalem
5.17-25	Wars with the Philistines

2 Samuel 6.1-7.29 God's Covenant with David

6.1-23	The Transfer of the Ark to Jerusalem
7.1-29	God's Promise to David

2 Samuel 8.1-18   David's Conquests

2 Samuel 9.1-20.26 The Reign of David

9.1-13	David Remembers his Covenant with Jonathan
10.1-19	War against the Ammonites
11.1-12.31	David and Bathsheba
13.1-22	The Rape of Tamar
13.23-39	Absalom's Revenge
14.1-33	Absalom's Return to Jerusalem
15.1-19.43	Absalom's Rebellion
20.1-25	Sheba's Rebellion

2 Samuel 21.1-24.25 Theological Summary

21.1-14	The Realities of Kingship
21.15-22	The Successful Warrior King
22.1-51	Kingship and a Sovereign God
23.1-7	Kingship and a Sovereign God
23.8-39	The Successful Warrior King
24.1-25	The Realities of Kingship

Hands on

Read the book of Haggai through five times in the manner suggested above, recording relevant notes and devising your own outline, complete with headings. Check out your outline with a commentary or Bible dictionary. Remember, Haggai is a small book, so you are looking for major divisions and natural subdivisions. You are not trying to break it up in great detail. We will do that kind of detailed break-up in Step 2.3: Structure.

Step 2.2

Literary Type

With books in hand, I strolled through the shopping centre, curious to see what was being paraded on the billboards and stands that littered the footpath. Having a wife who constantly loses keys (while I constantly lose glasses) I was immediately attracted by one stand promising an 'Amazing Whistling Key Ring' free. Naturally sceptical, my eyes rambled down the page past the large bold print to the ever smaller print as my eyes descended. As suspected, the word 'free' had been used rather loosely—the 'Amazing Whistling Key Ring' would cost me the price of two packs of batteries, an envelope, a stamp and a $5.00 cheque for postage and handling.

And then there was the newsagent, trying to suck me in with headlines. 'Reagan knew about arms deal', 'Sizzling Centrefold', 'Dangerous Di smashes bottle over Charles'. Avoiding dangerous Di and the sizzling centrefold, I invest in the paper. A quick glance down the first column tells me I was right—it is only rumoured by some obscure person (whose name I couldn't recognize) that Reagan really did know. Firm evidence is still being waited on. I skim through the paper to Hagar the Horrible and Footrot Flats and then to an editorial on the latest balance of payment figures. My serious reading done and destination arrived at (without running into someone while I walked reading the paper), I enter the cool of the

41

local library.

What was it I was here for? A thriller, some theology, a bit of light reading for Heather and a book that will tell me how to put together the pieces of the lawn mower I'd left lying on the back porch. Important things first—I wonder if John Le Carre has put out anything new recently? Maybe I could try that spy novelist Allan recommended, what was the name? Some name starting with P. That's it: Anthony Price.

And some satire for Heather. She must run out of P.G. Wodehouse soon. Here's one she hasn't read. Now for the kids. I'm sick of Mr Men, how about a bit of the Cat-in-the-Hat? Finally a manual for that rotten lawn mower.

This harmless series of events illustrates an important aspect of the interpretation of literature—discerning literary types. We live in a society that has a developed literary heritage and a multitude of literary types. Because we live amongst these types (or 'genres') we have learnt, by practice and education, to automatically engage a particular 'gear' as we read. When we read headlines, we have learnt to be suspicious until we read the first page. When we see 'sizzling' and 'centrefold' on a Playboy billboard we have a fair idea what is inside. On opening the paper and reading the comics, our minds engage another gear which enjoys and yet does not believe for a moment that there is a real Hagar the Horrible. Our minds switch to a serious, reflective mood as we read the editorial, again because our experience tells us that this literature is far different from Footrot Flats and ought to be treated differently.

We could go on through spy novels, P.G. Wodehouse, Dr Seuss and the lawn mower manual. We approach each of these 'genres' in a particular way and adopt different attitudes to them. In a sense, our minds have been conditioned to read in this way. Sometimes libraries help us by categorizing their literature into various classifications or by putting dust-jackets on books to help us identify them.

> *The Bible is the literary library of a nation, housing a host of different and largely uncategorized literary types.*

This type of thinking about literature is helpful for us when we approach the Bible. The Bible is the literary library of a nation, housing a host of different and largely uncategorized literary types.

Unfortunately we have usually been taught to read the Bible in only one gear, usually the one in which we read the Epistles of Paul. If we are going to understand what the original author wanted to say to the original hearers we must:

- recognize that there are a variety of literary genres in the Bible.
- learn to identify them.
- become acquainted with these various genres and the different ways of interpreting them.
- change the way we read as we come across these different literary types. We must learn to read prose as prose, poetry as poetry, history as history, fiction as fiction, letter as letter and prophecy as prophecy. We must avoid treating poetry as prose (and vice versa), history as fiction (and vice versa). To do otherwise would be as crazy as reading an Alistair Maclean novel as history, or a Romance as true life!

> ' *It would be as crazy as reading an Alistair Maclean novel as history, or a Romance as true life!*

Common Literary Genres

Here are some of the most common literary genres in the Scriptures:

Poetry
Law
Gospel
Prophecy
Narrative
Epistle
Psalm
Court Epic
History
Fictional Tale
Drama
Parable
Legend
Apocalyptic

Although it is helpful to recognize that the Bible is made up of different literary genres, we need to be careful that we don't classify too tightly. These genres can have subsets and at times they merge into each other. For example, Prophecy is very commonly written in poetic terms; Gospel and Epistle often contain sections of Apocalyptic; Parables are often found within the larger literary genre of Gospel; the Psalms contain laments, hymns and thanksgivings.

Examples

Let us look at some examples of how to interpret just three literary types: poetry, apocalyptic and parable.

Interpreting Poetry

Approximately one third of the Bible is written in formal poetry. Our modern translations do us the favour of indicating poetic sections by the way they are formatted.

Hebrew poetry is very rich, concise and repetitive. It is designed to be read aloud and read slowly. By its very nature, it is easy to memorize. Like all poetry, Hebrew poetry is a language of images. Like all poets, Hebrew poets do things with language and sentence structure that people do not ordinarily do when speaking. Although it uses most of the standard literary devices we would recognize from our own poetry (eg. assonance, simile, imagery, rhythm, metaphor), it is distinguished by its use of 'parallelism'.

Coming to grips with Hebrew poetic parallelism is essential if we are to accurately interpret the poetic sections of the Bible. Parallelism is not the be all and end all of Biblical poetry, but it is a very important component.

The unit of thought in Hebrew poetry is one verse. Each verse consists of a number of poetic lines, and each line contains two, three, four or more poetic phrases.

Take Psalm 103:3 as an example:

Who pardons   all your iniquities
Who heals   all your diseases

It is usual for each line in the verse to repeat, amplify, develop or contrast with the previous line. This pattern is called 'parallelism'. The lines run 'in parallel'. In general, interpreters of Biblical poetry recognize three forms of parallelism: Synonymous, Antithetic and Synthetic.

Some simple examples will help us understand each.

Synonymous parallelism

In this type of parallelism, latter lines repeat the thought of the first line. A complete parallelism occurs where there is a complete correspondence between the thought of line 1 and that of line 2.

That is:

Line 1   [A   ]   [B   ]

Line 2   [A¹]   [B¹]

We see this in Psalm 24:1-3.

The earth is the Lord's   and everything in it
The world   and all who live in it

For he founded it   upon the seas
And established it   upon the waters

Who may ascend   the hill of the Lord
Who may stand   in his holy place

Antithetic parallelism

As with synonymous parallelism, the writer expresses the same or similar thought in subsequent lines, but this time by using opposites (eg. 'foolish/wise' instead of 'foolish/lacking judgment'). The same thought is expressed, but from two different perspectives. The lines are balanced, but through opposition or contrast. We are most familiar with antithetic parallelism from the book of Proverbs.

Look at Proverbs 9:9 as an example:

A wicked messenger   falls into trouble
but a trustworthy envoy   brings healing

Note the contrasts: wicked/trustworthy and trouble/healing. Note also that the same point is being made through contrast.

Synthetic Parallelism

In Synthetic Parallelism, line two completes the thought of line one. Psalm 65 holds some good examples of Synthetic Parallelism:

line 1   Praise awaits you, O God, in Zion
line 2   to you our vows will be fulfilled.

line 1   When we were overwhelmed by sins
line 2   you forgave our transgressions.

Each of the examples above demonstrate complete parallelism, but parallelism is often not complete. In other words, sometimes the second line omits a part of the first line because it is understood and therefore unnecessary.

Psalm 61:1 contains an example of incomplete parallelism:

Hear my cry	O Lord
Attend unto my prayer	(understood)

The three types of parallelism listed above are the basic building blocks of Hebrew poetry. Scholars have refined these categories and classified even more, but these three are a solid place to start. For a fuller explanation of how to understand and interpret Biblical poetry you could read *How to Read the Psalms* by Tremper Longman (IVP).

However, even with the basic ideas we have gathered here, we can come up with some rules of interpretation for this genre. For example:

✔ DO ... realize that each of the lines in Hebrew poetry are not self contained but belong with at least one other line. When you hear one line, wait for the next and take them as together making a point.

✘ DON'T... misunderstand the message of the verse by taking every word (or phrase) to mean something in its own right.

Interpreting Apocalyptic

Apocalyptic literature is a type of literature with a definite kind of theology, composed mostly by Jews and Jewish Christians from the days of the Babylonian Exile (or perhaps slightly before) onwards. Traces of it can be found in the Old Testament (some of the Prophets and in some of the later Psalms) and in the New Testament (Mark 13; 2 Thessalonians 2; Revelation).

It was almost always composed in times of trial or crisis and was intended as a kind of private comfort for believers. Because of this, it developed doctrines and used forms of expression that sounded somewhat strange, if not bizarre, in more ordinary times.

Biblical apocalyptic writing saw itself as the child of

> *Biblical apocalyptic writing saw itself as the child of prophecy.*

prophecy. This can be seen in its reliance upon the prophetic writings as a source of thought, language, imagery and symbolism. Apocalyptic writers take the promises of the prophets and reassert them for their own time.

There are two basic ideas within apocalyptic thinking:
- the struggle between good and evil
- the belief in two ages (the present evil age and the age to come).

In order to convey these basic ideas and speak dramatically to a people under severe stress, the writers of apocalyptic developed a highly symbolic literary style to convey their message of hope.

The usual manner of presentation was a vision or series of visions told with these exaggerated symbols. Animals were used to represent nations, and horns to represent power or a person who exercised power. Colours and numbers became symbols for certain things.

Only a few numbers were used (eg 3, $3\frac{1}{2}$, 4, 5, 6, 7, 10, 12 and their multiples, squares and cubes). 3 is often taken to stand for the spirit world (good or evil), while 4 is the earth number (eg. four corners of the earth). If you add 3 and 4 you get the complete or perfect number, 7. One half of 7 (ie. $3\frac{1}{2}$) is the incomplete number, the number of something that is cut off or limited.

Only a few colours were used and they too usually had their symbolic value. For example, white conveyed victory (not purity), red conveyed strife (usually war), and pale (literally 'greenish grey', the colour of a corpse) naturally conveyed death.

Two basic errors are often made in interpreting apocalyptic imagery. On the one hand, people take them too literally. They see that the number of the elect in Revelation is 144,000 and take that to mean that God will chose 144,000 people to be Christians—no more, no less. The other mistake is to take the imagery figuratively but to forget that it uses symbols that were never intended to be images. For example, when John gives us a vision of Christ in Revelation 1* he does not want us merely to conjure up the image in our minds. He is conveying a symbolic impression of the majesty of Christ. Similarly, the dragon in the book of Revelation is not intended to be sketched—he stands for an idea.

Again, even with a simple understanding of apocalyp-

I turned around to see the voice that was speaking to me. And when I turned I saw seven golden lampstands, and among the lampstands was someone "like a son of man," dressed in a robe reaching down to his feet and with a golden sash around his chest. His head and hair were white like wool, as white as snow, and his eyes were like flazing fire. His feet were like bronze glowing in a furnace, and his voice was like the sound of rushing waters. In his right hand he held seven stars, and out of his mouth came a sharp double-edged sword. His face was like the sun shining in all its brilliance.

Revelation 1:12-16

tic literature we can come up with some basic rules of interpretation for this genre. For example:

✘ DON'T ... take everything too literally

✔ DO ... become familiar with the meaning of the symbols used, both in terms of their contemporary usage and their Biblical background.

✔ DO ... try and understand the idea/s being conveyed through the symbols.

✔ DO ... study the historical background of the writings.

Interpreting Parables

A Parable is a metaphor or simile which compares a religious truth with a common experience or circumstance in life.

Jesus often used parables to teach the meaning of his own life and ministry, and the nature of the kingdom of God.

> ' *Parables are a punchy form of communication designed to creep up on you without your knowing it. They are like time bombs.*

Parables are a punchy form of communication designed to creep up on you without your knowing it. They are like time bombs. They look innocuous and are therefore received quite readily, only to go off suddenly and shatter your way of looking at life. One of the best Biblical examples of a parable is the masterpiece addressed to King David by Nathan the prophet in 2 Samuel 12:1-7. It had one point, and it caught the hearer totally unawares. You can see that the details were unimportant. As with other parables, the details are there simply to help the speaker get his message across.

Nathan's parable illustrates another important point about parables—they are not designed to be an intellectual exercise. When Jesus used parables he was not so much concerned with intellectual stimulation as with stirring up a moral or spiritual response on the part of the hearers. He wasn't conveying deep, esoteric information that only the initiated could understand. He was after a decisive response of repentance, belief and obedience.

Therefore, some basic DOs and DON'Ts for interpreting parables are:

✘ DON'T make everything mentioned in the parable equal something else (ie. don't allegorize!).

✔ DO ... look at the real life context of the parable.

✔ DO ... ask, 'What are the unusual elements of the story that would have struck the original hearers with force?'

✔ DO ... look for theme/s of the parable (nb. often found in the last line!).
✔ DO ... ask, 'Who was the parable intended for and what effect was it intended to have on them?'

1

What 'genres' are present in the book of Haggai? Where?

2

Read the article on 'prophecy' in *The New Bible Dictionary*. From your reading work out:
   (i) special characteristics of prophecy
       eg. Prophecy is closely connected with history

(ii) rules for the interpretation of prophecy.
eg. DO ... take the words of the prophets in their usual literal sense, unless the context or the manner in which they are fulfilled clearly indicate that they have a symbolical meaning.

[For help in this question and in working out rules of interpretation for different literary types, a helpful, easy to read book is *Knowing Scripture* (IVP) by RC Sproul. An even easier book is by C Wright, *Users Guide to the Bible* (Lion). Those wanting to do some more extensive work could consult Joel B Green's book *How to Read Prophecy* (IVP).]

3

Classify the numbered passages with the appropriate literary types. (Write the numbers of the passages next to the literary types.)

Apocalyptic Visions ....

Genealogies ....

Historical Narratives..

Hymns of Praise ....

Instructional Wisdom ....

Laments..

Laws and Statutes..

Prophetic Oracle ....

Riddle ....

Song ....

Taunts ....

Thanksgivings ....

Proverbial wisdom sayings ....

1) I will sing to the Lord, for he is highly exalted. The horse and its rider he has hurled into the sea. The Lord is my strength and my song; He has become my salvation. He is my God, and I will praise him, my father's God, and I will exalt him.

2) Each of you must respect his mother and father, and you must observe my Sabbaths. I am the Lord your God. Do not turn to idols or make gods of cast metal for yourselves. I am the Lord your God.

3) When Moses sent them to explore Canaan, he said, "Go up through the Negev and on into the hill country. See what the land is like and whether the people who live there are strong or weak, few or many. What kind of land do they live in? Is it good or bad? What kind of towns do they live in? Are they unwalled or fortified? How is the soil? Is it fertile or poor? Are there trees on it or not? Do your best to bring back some of the fruit of the land." (It was the season for the first ripe grapes.) So they went up and explored the land from the desert or Zin as far as Rehob, toward Lebo Hamath. They went up through the Negev and came to Hebron, where Ahiman, Shashai and Talmai, the descendants of Anak, lived.

4) "Out of the eater, something to eat; out of the strong, something sweet." For three days they could not give the answer.

5) Perez was the father of Hezron, Hezron the father of Ram, Ram the father of Amminadab, Amminadab the father of Nahashon, Nahashon the father of Salmon, Salmon the father of Obed, Obed the father of Jesse, and Jesse the father of David.

6) Then the commander stood and called out in Hebrew: "Hear the word of the great king, the king of Assyria! This is what the king says: 'Do not let Hezekiah deceive you. He cannot deliver you from my hand. Do not let Hezekiah persuade you to trust in the Lord when he says, "The Lord will surely deliver us; this city will not be given into the hand of the king of Assyria."... Who of all the gods of these countries has been able to save his land from me? How then can the Lord deliver Jerusalem from my hand?'"

7) Give thanks to the Lord, call on his name; make known among the nations what he has done. Sing to him, sing praise to him; tell of all his wonderful acts. Glory in his holy name; let the hearts of those who seek the Lord rejoice.

8) If your enemy is hungry, give him food to eat; if he is thirsty, give him water to drink. In doing this, you will heap burning coals on his head, and the Lord will reward you.

9) Charm is deceptive, and beauty is fleeting; but a woman who fears the Lord is to be praised.

10) Sing to the Lord a new song, his praise from the ends of the earth, you who go down to the sea, and all that is in it, you islands, and all who live in them. Let the desert and its towns raise their voices; let the settlements where Kedar lives rejoice.

11) We have sinned and rebelled and you have not forgiven. You have covered yourself with anger and pursued us; you have slain without pity. You have covered yourself with a cloud so that no prayer can get through. You have made us scum and refuse among the nations.

13) As I looked at the living creatures, I saw wheels on the ground beside each creature with its four faces. This was the appearance and structure of the wheels: they sparkled like chrysolite and all four looked alike. Each appeared to be made like a wheel intersecting a wheel. As they moved, they would go in any one of the four directions the creatures faced; the wheels did not turn about as the creatures went. Their rims were high and awesome, and all four rims were full of eyes all round.

14) This is the interpretation, O king, and this is the decree the Most High has issued against my lord the king: You will be driven away from people and will live with wild animals; you will eat grass like cattle and be drenched with the dew of heaven. Seven times will pass by until you acknowledge that the Most High is sovereign over the kingdoms of men and gives them to anyone he wishes.

Step 2.3

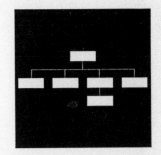

Structure

Interpretation is all about communication. And communication, spoken or written, is tied up with structure. In language, 'structure' is the way that you arrange words, phrases, clauses, sentences, paragraphs, and even larger compositions, to achieve a given purpose.

Most of the time the structure of what we say is unconscious. However, sometimes it is deliberate and very conscious. Either way, the structure of what we say conveys information about ourselves and forms part of what we want to say.

Psalm 119 is a very good Scriptural example of the use of structure to convey meaning and to give added emphasis to the content. The first thing the Hebrew reader notices is that the author has a very definite structure in mind. The poem is an acrostic poem: the first eight verses begin with the first letter of the Hebrew alphabet; the second eight verses begin with the second letter of the alphabet; and so on, through the whole Hebrew alphabet. The whole Psalm, in terms of content, is a praise of the law, the word of God, and the joys to be found in keeping it. By setting out the psalm in this way, the author reminds us of the fullness of the word of God and that it is the essence of all of life.

Although Paul often gets carried away in his arguments and begins to extol God or go off on a tangent, his letters also betray a structure that is very important in

' *Whether*
conscious or
unconscious, the
way a writer has
structured what he
says communicates
meaning and gives
impact.

understanding his writing. You will often find that Paul spends the first half of a letter spelling out the gospel before drawing out its implications for the lives of his hearers. This change from doctrine to its implications (and his exhortation to change) is often heralded by the words 'therefore' or 'then' (as in Romans 12:1-2; Ephesians 4:1; Colossians 3:1). The structure of Paul's writing tells us important things about his understanding of the basis for Christian ethical decisions: they are to be based on the gospel, on what God has done for us in Christ.

Whether conscious or unconscious, the way a writer has structured what he says communicates meaning and gives impact. Analysing structure will therefore be an important part of determining what the original author intended to say to the original readers/hearers, and how he intended them to react to what he said. Remember that structures can be quite prominent (eg. Psalm 119), or quite unobtrusive (eg. parts of the Gospels), but are quite often significant.

There are various levels of structure in the Bible. At the top end we have the structure of the Bible itself, which tells us a lot about how people viewed its contents and how they thought it ought to be read. In Step 2.1, we looked at another level—the structure of a book—and worked out how to analyse it.

Other levels include major sections within the book (eg. Genesis 1-11; 12-50), smaller sections (eg. chapters), sentences and phrases.

The aim of this study is to analyse the structure of Bible passages. The importance of sentence structure will be covered in Step 2.4 on 'Meaning'.

Presuming we have broken a book into smaller, manageable sections for more detailed study, what should we do and what should we look for?

(NB. For this exercise, as for all detailed work on a passage, you should use a more more literal translation of the Bible such as the *New American Standard Bible* or the *Revised Standard Version*.)

Look for patterns within the passage

Photocopy the passage and invest in some coloured pens. Use them to mark in the following:
■ repetitions of words

■ changes in the person being talked about (eg. changes from 'he/she' to 'I' or 'you', or from 'they' to 'me' or 'you')
■ ideas that are dropped and then resumed later
■ parallelism
■ central or pivotal words
■ word associations
■ key ideas
■ comparisons
■ contrasts
■ progressions or digressions
■ cause and effect arguments

In all of this, the key elements are 'repetition' and 'progression' (ie. where a word or idea is developed progressively through the passage).

Look for the natural flow of the passage

With pen in hand, ask yourself:
■ How does the passage start?
■ How does it proceed?
■ How does it come to an end?
■ Does the structure seem to bear any relation the meaning of the passage?
■ Is the impact of the passage at least partly related to its structure?
■ Is there any inherent logic to the passage?

Put all your findings together

Ask yourself (again, jotting down your thoughts and conclusions):
■ What is the passage emphasizing?
■ Why has the writer ordered the words and ideas the way he has?
■ What is being stressed?
■ Is there anything that really stands out about the structure (eg. elements that are beautiful, striking, jarring, offensive, unexpected, unique)?

Perhaps a 'flow chart' of the thoughts of the passage might be a good way of putting this all together.

If appropriate, reflect your findings in a breakup of the passage

That is, work out some headings for the various sections of the passage that help demonstrate the structure of the passage (Remember that your headings, like those put in by some Bibles, are not part of the Bible!).

Compare your findings with a commentary

Look up a commentary or Bible dictionary and see if their analysis gives you any fresh insights. Change your findings if you think it is necessary, but don't feel compelled to bow before the authority of the commentator.

Some cautions:

✗ BE CAREFUL!
Structure IS a device often used by the author to convey meaning and make an impact. Structure CAN BE an aid for the interpreter to determine meaning and impact. But don't force structure where it is not intended to be. Not every passage has a neat structure.

✗ DON'T MISS THE POINT!
Our aim is not to break up the text into tiny pieces so that it loses its impact. The structure must be left intact so that its force upon us is maintained.

✗ DON'T OVERDO IT!
Those of us who like toying with words, analysing structural patterns, and playing with coloured pencils and highlighters, need to realize that structure is but one means the author can use. Some authors convey meaning and impact by painting pictures in words for us. Their writing is often loose and unstructured. To tighten it up would be to destroy it. Sometimes you may find both within the same book. The book of Revelation, for example, relies heavily on both structure and imagery.

Examples

Below are some suggested structures for a selection of passages from Scripture. I hope that it is apparent that these structures are not artificial but grow naturally out of the passage itself. Note, particularly, how repetition and progression play an important part in determining the structure of these passages. The example of Psalm 46 shows how the whole process—from analysis of structure through to interpretation and application—might proceed.

Matthew 18:21-35

Verse 21	The question is posed
Verse 22	The question is answered in the positive
Verses 23-35	The question is posed and answered in the negative

    The Parable

          Scene 1   23-27 The Pardoning Master
          Scene 2   28-30 The Punishing Servant
          Scene 3   31-34 The Punishing Master

Verse 35   Application

James 2:14-26

2.14	*The Question:* Can faith save if it claims to exist without deeds?
2.15-17	*Illustration 1:* The Hungry Brother Conclusion: Faith that doesn't change the way you act towards others is counterfeit
2.18-19	*Illustration 2:* A Troubled Demon Conclusion: Faith that doesn't issue in a changed attitude to God is counterfeit
2.20-24	*Illustration 3:* Abraham, the friend of God Conclusion: Genuine faith responds to God and acts accordingly
2.25-26	*Illustration 4:* A Welcoming Prostitute Conclusion: Genuine faith changes the way you act towards others

57

Psalm 46

Same Hebrew word:
created world falls (2)
nations fall (6)
God's city doesn't fall (5)

1 God is our refuge and strength,
    an ever present <u>help</u> in trouble.
2 therefore we will not fear, though <u>the earth</u> give way
    and the mountains fall into the heart of the sea,
3 though its waters roar and foam
    and the mountains quake with their surging.

Selah

Q: How did they know God was with them?
A: The city had the temple and the Ark which symbolized God's presence.

4 There is a river whose streams make glad the city of God,
    the holy place where the Most High dwells.
5 God is within her, she will not fall.
    God will help her at break of day.
6 Nations are in uproar, kingdoms fall,
    he lifts his voice, <u>the earth</u> melts.
7 The Lord Almighty is with us;
    the God of Jacob is our fortress.

Selah

8 come and see the works of the Lord,
    the desolations he has brought on <u>the earth</u>.
9 He makes wars to cease to the ends of <u>the earth</u>;
    he breaks the bow and shatters the spear,
    he burns the shields with fire.

Hebrew is 'Immanu-Yahweh' (Yahweh is with us). Similar to name of Jesus 'Immanu-El' (God is with us)—see Matt. 1:23

10 'Be still and know that I am God;
    I will be exalted among the nations,
    I will be exalted in <u>the earth</u>.'
11 The Lord Almighty is with us;
    the God of Jacob is our fortress.

Selah

Break-up of Psalm ('Selah' divides the sections): 1-3 *God, the Lord of creation, is with us*
    4-7 *God, the Lord of the nations, is with us*
    8-11 *God, the Lord of history, is with us*

Meaning: The psalm shows the earth and the nations fighting against God and his people. The created order ('earth') will 'fall' (2). The nations will 'fall' (6). BUT the city of God will NOT 'fall' (5) because God is with it. Therefore, Israel should stop struggling to determine her own destiny apart from God, and know that God will triumph over the created order and the nations, and help her.

Application: We often feel that everyone and everything is set against us. We feel tempted to determine our own destiny. But we should cease struggling and realize that God is with us in Jesus (ie. Immanuel) and that he will eventually triumph and we with him.

Hands on

1

On the following pages you will find the book of Haggai typed out. You have already broken Haggai into major sections in Step 2.1 Getting Acquainted. Now, using the methods outlined in this study, analyse the structure of each of these major sections. Feel free to write in this book with pens, highlighters or coloured pencils. There is plenty of space around the text for this purpose. If you prefer, photocopy some extra copies and work on those.

Haggai

In the second year of Darius the king, on the first day of the sixth month, the word of the Lord came by the prophet Haggai to Zerubbabel the son of Shealtiel, governor of Judah, and to Joshua the son of Jehozadak, the high priest, saying, "Thus says the Lord of hosts, 'This people says, "The time has not come, even the time for the house of the Lord to be rebuilt."'" Then the word of the Lord came by Haggai the prophet saying, "Is it time for you yourselves to dwell in your panelled houses while this house lies desolate?" Now therefore, thus says the Lord of hosts, "Consider your ways! You have sown much, but harvest little; you eat, but there is not enough to be satisfied; you drink, but there is not enough to become drunk; you put on clothing, but no one is warm enough; and he who earns, earns wages to put into a purse with holes." Thus says the Lord of hosts, "Consider your ways! Go up to the mountain, bring wood and rebuild the house, that I may be pleased with it and be glorified," says the Lord. "You look for much, but behold it comes to little; when you bring it home, I blow it away. Why?" declares the Lord of hosts, "Because of my house which lies desolate, while each of you runs to his own house. Therefore, because of you the sky has withheld its dew, and the earth has withheld its produce. And I called for a drought on the land, on the mountains, on the grain, on the new wine, on the oil, on what the ground produces, on men, on cattle, and on all the labour of your hands." Then Zerubbabel the son of Shealtiel, and Joshua the son of Jehozadak, the high priest, with all the remnant of the people, obeyed the voice of the Lord their God and the words of Haggai the prophet, as the Lord their God had sent him. And the people showed reverence for the Lord. Then Haggai, the messenger of the Lord, spoke by the commission of the Lord to the people saying, "'I am with you,' declares the Lord." So the Lord stirred up the spirit of Zerubbabel the son of Shealtiel, governor of Judah, and the spirit of Joshua the son of Jehozadak, the high priest, and the spirit of all the remnant of the people; and they came and worked on the house of the Lord God of hosts, their God, on the twenty-fourth day of the sixth month in the second year of Darius the king. On the twenty-first of the seventh month, the word of the Lord came by Haggai the prophet saying, "Speak now to Zerubbabel the son of Shealtiel, governor of Judah, and to Joshua the son of Jehozadak, the high priest, and to the remnant of the people saying, 'Who is left among you who saw this temple in its former glory? And how do you see it now? Does it not seem to you like nothing in comparison? But now take courage, Zerubbabel,' declares the Lord, 'take courage also, Joshua son of Jehozadak, the high priest, and all you people of the land take courage,' declares the Lord, 'and work; for I am with you,' says the Lord of hosts. 'As for the promise which I made you when you came out of Egypt, my spirit is abiding in your midst; do not fear!' For thus says the Lord of hosts, 'Once more in a little while, I am going to shake the heavens and the earth, the sea also and the dry land. And I will shake all the nations; and they will come with the wealth of the nations; and I will fill this house with glory,' says the Lord of hosts. 'The silver is mine, and the gold is mine,' declares the Lord of hosts. 'The latter glory of this house will be greater than the former,' says the Lord of hosts, 'and in this place I shall give peace,' declares the Lord of hosts." On the twenty-fourth day of the ninth month, in the second year of Darius, the word of the Lord came to Haggai the prophet saying, "Thus says the Lord of hosts, 'Ask now the priests for a ruling: If a man carries holy meat in the fold of his garment, and touches bread with this fold, or cooked food, wine, oil, or any other food, will it become holy?'" And the priests answered and said, "No." Then Haggai said, "If one who is unclean from a corpse touches any of these, will the latter become unclean?" And the priests answered and said, "It will become unclean." Then Haggai answered and said, "'So is this people. And so is this nation before me,' declares the Lord, 'and so is every work of their hands; and what they offer is unclean. But now, do consider from this day onward: before one stone was placed on another in the temple of the Lord, from that time when one came to a grain heap of twenty measures, there would be only ten; and when one came to the wine vat to draw fifty measures, there would only be twenty. I smote you and every work of your hands with blasting wind, mildew, and hail; yet you did not come back to me,' declares the Lord. 'Do consider from this day onward, from the twenty-fourth day of the ninth month; from the day when the temple of the Lord was founded, consider: Is the seed still in the barn? Even including the vine, the fig tree, the pomegranate, and the olive tree, it has not borne fruit. Yet from this day on I will bless you.'" Then the word of the Lord came a second time to Haggai on the twenty-fourth day of the month saying, "Speak to Zerubbabel governor of Judah, saying, 'I am going to shake the heavens and the earth. And I will overthrow the thrones of kingdoms and destroy the power of the kingdoms of the nations; and I will overthrow the chariots and their riders will go down, every one by the sword of another. On that day,' declares the Lord of hosts, 'I will take you, Zerubbabel, son of Shealtiel, my servant,' declares the Lord, 'and I will make you like a signet ring, for I have chosen you,'" declares the Lord of hosts.

(from *The New American Standard Bible*)

2

Using the methods outlined in this step analyse the structure of the Psalm 1.

Psalm 1

How blessed is the man who does not walk in the counsel of the wicked, nor stand in the path of sinners, nor sit in the seat of scoffers!

But his delight is in the law of the LORD, and in his law he meditates day and night.

And he wil be like a tree firmly planted by streams of water, which yields its fruit in its season, and its leaf does not wither; and in whatever he does, he prospers.

The wicked are not so. But they are like chaff which the wind drives away.

Therefore the wicked will not stand in the judgment, nor sinners in the assembly of the righteous.

For the LORD knows the way of the righteous, but the way of the wicked will perish.

(from *The New American Standard Bible*)

Step 2.4

Meaning

The icy wind of Melbourne cut through me like cold steel. As I waited for the train, I browsed the new wave graffiti that covered every inch of the freshly painted ticket box—a symbol of an endless battle for supremacy.

But wait...there! In the middle of that sentence. A word not met. A new word, not yet defined in my Macquarie Dictionary. A word fresh from the fevered imagination of some fifteen-year-old, with nothing to do and nowhere to go in the early hours of yet another sun free day.

All day that word bothered me. What did it mean? Where could I go to find out?

If you wanted to find out the meaning of new word you had just discovered on a ticket office door in some inner city suburb in Melbourne, what would you do? Where would you go to find out?

Probably your first thought would be to find out the meaning from the context of the sentence. A second option would be to hide somewhere on the train station at 3.00 am, capture this anonymous fifteen-year-old graffitist, and ask him. Presuming that this was inconvenient, perhaps you could browse other walls on the station and nearby ones, attempting to find other occurrences of its use.

Another option would be to find a group of people that he/she spends time with. You could wander through the neighbourhood looking for the sorts of people that you figure would be likely to spend their idle moments inscribing their initials and messages upon train ticket offices. Upon finding such people, you could ask them if they had any idea as to the meaning of the word.

You could also ask people in general who live in the neighbourhood. Maybe they have heard the word in use somewhere and know its meaning?

Moving further afield, you could ask the people you were staying with in another suburb of Melbourne, even if they don't frequent railway stations in the early hours of the morning. There is, however, a diminishing chance of coming up with a promising meaning using this course of action.

You could even ask your wife/husband when you return home to Sydney, and other people as you travel round Australia in the ensuing year or so. Once again, your possibility of success is limited and diminishing rapidly.

Finally, you could ask your friend living in Chicago, in the United States, when you visit him in a month's time. However, unless the graffitist is an escapee from downtown Chicago, there is very little chance that your friend will know anything about the meaning of some obscure word used by street graffitists at 3.00 am on a freezing morning in inner city Melbourne.

It makes sense, doesn't it? The meaning of a particular word is most closely determined by the context in which it originally occurs. As you move out in concentric circles to more distant people, the possibility of finding meaning is also more distant. Meaning is best determined by its most immediate context.

It is like this with the Bible. If you are reading a passage of the Bible and come across a word you don't understand, then the way to determine its meaning is to start with the most immediate context and work outwards, placing the most stress upon the most immediate context.

> *The meaning of a particular word is most closely determined by the context in which it originally occurs.*

The meaning of words

What sort of words am I looking for?

When we read our Bibles we come across two sorts of words that need clarification:

- words which are completely new to us (eg. 'propitiation', 'gleanings', 'behemoth')
- words which we have encountered before and which already have some meaning because of our prior knowledge (eg. 'grace', 'love', 'peace').

In the second category, the words are significant and require clarification for a number of reasons. They may be significant because they are theologically loaded (eg. 'hope', 'righteousness'), or because they clearly make a difference to the meaning of the passage (eg. 'body' in 1 Thessalonians 4:4). They might be important because they are 'catch words' which are repeated throughout the passage (eg. 'boast' in 2 Corinthians 10-12). Sometimes, words which would normally be insignificant become very significant because of their context in the passage you are looking at (eg. the word 'work' as a technical term for Paul's ministry).

What do I do when I have found them?

The procedure for dealing with both sorts of words is similar, although new words need some additional information.

1) Establish a broad range of meaning

When you come across a new word you should firstly establish a broad range of meaning for it. This can be done using a dictionary (Hebrew, Greek, or even English). This gives you a starting point for determining its meaning in the context of the passage.

However, as with familiar words, we must place stress on the meaning that comes from the immediate context, not on the dictionary. We must be ready to sacrifice the meaning we have brought from outside if the most immediate context demands it.

Once you have established a broad range of meaning for the word, you can proceed in the following manner, continually asking yourself:

- Does the term have a technical meaning?
- Is it always used in apparently the same manner?
- Are there shades of meaning in its usage?
- In what type of literature does it occur?
- Is its meaning literal or metaphorical?

*2) Look at the passage in which
the word appears.*

See if the context helps with the meaning of the word.

*3) Look to see if the word is used elsewhere in the same
document.*

What does it mean there? Again, see if the immediate context helps with the meaning of the word in these passages.

4) Look at other writings by the same person.

How does the author use the word elsewhere?

5) Look at other people writing at the same time.

How did they use the word? What did it mean to them?

6) Look at other people writing at the same time, from similar backgrounds and under similar influences.

Do they use the word? How do they use it? What does it mean to them? Especially check out any parallel passages to the one you are looking at (eg. 1 Corinthians 11:23-25 cf Matthew 26:26-28; Mark 14:22-24; Luke 22:17-20).

It is easy to see how this applies to the Bible. For example, Paul and Peter are writing at the same time. They are both Jews influenced by the Old Testament and by Jesus. They are both Christians.

7) Consider the writings/teachings of other people whose words or teaching have significantly influenced the author.

Did they use the word? What did it mean to them?

Again the Bible provides many examples of places where these sorts of considerations apply. For example, Paul and Peter are heavily dependent upon the teaching of Jesus. Their use of words and ideas will have been influenced by his ideas and teachings (especially in the area of theological terminology and ethical application).

8) Consider other literary sources that may have influenced the author.

What other literary sources are there? Do they make use of words like this? What do they mean by the word when they use it? Do these other sources appear to have influenced the author's usage in your passage?

68

Remember not to restrict your work to the same part of speech. If you are looking at a noun in your passage, don't forget to chase up the verb or adjective with the same meaning. For example, if you are looking at what Paul means by 'faith', also look at how he uses the words 'faithfulness' and 'to believe'.

If you have done all this, your 'range of meaning' will have undergone a shift. It may have become broader, or it may have tightened up considerably. If you had gone through the process with the word 'grace', for example, your exploration of both the Old and New Testaments may have led you to think that the definition 'God's unmerited favour' lacks a bit of punch, especially when compared to how it might have struck a first century Jew used to the Hebrew word *hesed* (meaning 'lovingkindness', 'covenant love', 'loyalty').

Now that your range of meaning has sharpened up and the background to the use of your word has become a bit clearer, go back and look at the word in its context. Do your first tentative conclusions still stand? What meaning now makes the most sense here? Remember the aim of this exercise: to find the meaning of *this word* in *this context*.

Notice that we only suggest looking up the Old Testament when trying to find the meaning of a New Testament word. The reason is obvious: the New Testament could not have influenced the use of a word in the Old Testament. Influence can only flow from older sources to newer ones and not vice versa.

> ❛ *Remember the aim of this exercise: to find the meaning of* this *word* in *this* context.

Aids for finding meanings

Bible Dictionaries & Encyclopaedias

Bible Dictionaries and Encyclopedias are a veritable mine of Biblical information (and trivia!). They are usually alphabetically arranged and contain articles treating important Biblical ideas, books, words, people and concepts. They are designed to give a general grasp of the issues involved. They also usually give an extended bibliography for those interested in doing further reading.

A good basic dictionary is the *Lion Handbook to the Bible*. A bit more technical and fuller is *The New Bible Dictionary* or its illustrated, three volume equivalent *The*

Illustrated Bible Dictionary. (There is aso a new concise version of *The New Bible Dictionary* available.) I would class a *New Bible Dictionary* as an essential tool for systematic, informed Bible study.

Biblical Wordbooks and Lexicons

At another level there are Biblical wordbooks and lexicons. These convey much more specific, detailed information about what words mean by looking at their usage in the Old and New Testaments and in literature of the time.

There are a number of such wordbooks for those using English translations. The best of these, although a trifle technical, is *The New International Dictionary of New Testament Theology.*

Biblical Concordances

A Biblical concordance is a necessity for doing the sort of things advocated in this step. In the hands of someone who is used to it, a concordance is a sophisticated and invaluable tool. It enables the user to trace how a word is used throughout the Bible. Almost all established translations of the Bible now have an extensive concordance readily available.

Cross Reference Bibles

Another helpful aid in interpreting the Bible is a good cross reference Bible. A cross reference Bible takes key words or ideas in the passage you are reading and gives cross references to other passages where the same word or idea is used. Cross references will also point to parallel passages, or passages which may have influenced the thought of the writer at this point. An experienced user of a cross reference Bible can look up a whole chain of related passages or ideas through the use of the cross references. The best cross reference Bibles are those which have been compiled by a group of people rather than an individual, as the latter may be influenced by the prejudices of the compiler.

English Dictionaries

A note needs to be made regarding English dictionaries. While these may be used to establish an initial, temporary meaning, we need to be careful. The words in the Bible are Hebrew and Greek words which have been translated into English. Many of the terms are part of a technical vocabulary (eg. 'covenant', 'repentance') and definitions of such terms in standard English dictionaries will be adequate at only the most basic level.

A Basic Library

I would suggest the following as a basic library for someone wanting to study the Bible well:
■ A good general reading Bible (eg. NIV)
■ A more literal word-for-word translation of the Bible (eg. RV, RSV, NASB) with cross references. Second-hand copies can be picked up cheaply in good second-hand bookshops.
■ An extensive concordance for use with your more literal translation.
■ A *New Bible Dictionary*.

Things to remember

Remember that the immediate context is the most important factor in determining the meaning of a passage.

Just because a word is never used in a particular way anywhere else doesn't mean it can't mean that here. Language is not based on statistics, but on usage. Words function in a context, not on their own.

Remember not to go overboard in analysing a word.

Don't make too much of specific words in a particular context. Like us, the authors of the Bible did not always choose their words as carefully as our analysis seems to presuppose. There is often a better reason for why an author used a word than its bare meaning. It might have sounded better, or fitted better with the other words in the sentence, or rhymed, or have been a synonym for another word.

Don't forget Grammar.

In ordinary circumstances we do not utter isolated words or phrases, but whole sentences. Remember that although every sentence must be composed of words, not every string of words is a sentence. Knowing the meaning of individual words is no guarantee that you know what the sentence means. The meaning of a sentence is dependent upon how those words are strung together.

71

Examples

'Knowing Good and Evil' in Genesis 3

The first few chapters of the Bible raise many problems for the interpreter, not least of which is the phrase 'the knowledge of good and evil' (eg. in Genesis 3:5, 22). The immediate context helps us somewhat with the interpretation of the phrase but there still remains little certainty as to the meaning.

However, if the words 'knowing good and evil' occur elsewhere in the Old Testament then it may be that their usage will be similar to that used in Genesis 1-3 or at least will reflect the usage in Genesis 1-3.

A quick survey of a concordance will point out a number of references to the words (eg. Deuteronomy 1:39; 2 Samuel 14:17; 2 Samuel 19:35; 1 Kings 3:9).

Deuteronomy 1:39 talks about children who are under a particular age (ie. the age when they 'know good and evil'). The implication is that 'knowing good and evil' has to do with making moral judgments.

In 2 Samuel 14 David is being asked to perform his kingly duty of pronouncing judgment on a particular case where there appears to be compassionate grounds for waiving the requirements of the law. David is being asked to give his ruling ('word' in verse 17). The woman then pronounces that David is able to do this since he is like an angel of God in 'knowing good and evil'. The implication is that David is in the place of God, able to pronounce what is good or evil. He is the determiner of good and evil in this situation.

2 Samuel 19:35 is not unlike Deuteronomy 1:39 although here it has to do with age rather than youth, with physically seeing and hearing rather than moral perception. 'Knowing good and evil' appears to be the ability (or lack of ability) to sense good and bad food, male and female singers, and so on.

1 Kings 3:9 is like 2 Samuel 14. It has to do with governing or making decisions on behalf of God regarding his people. The king is asking for discernment so that

> *I am now eighty years old. Can I tell the difference between what is good and what is not? Can your servant taste what he eats and drinks? Can I still hear the voices of men and women singers? Why should your servant be an added burden to my lord the King?*
> *2 Samuel 19:35*

he might judge rightly. He is asking for wisdom so that he can decide between right and wrong, good and evil.

If we take the meanings from 2 Samuel and 1 Kings and try them out in Genesis 2-3, it makes great sense.

When God creates mankind and puts them in the garden, God is the determiner of what is good and evil. In eating the forbidden fruit, man is saying that he does not want God to be the determiner of what is good and evil, but that man is to be the determiner. This is how man becomes "like God knowing good and evil" (3:22). This is the essence of sin—to discard the rule of God and assert the right to determine what is good and what is bad on your own.

'Godliness' in 1 Timothy 4:8

1) Establish a broad range of meaning

In this case we can start off with the broad meaning of the word as it is used in common English. A godly person is a person who acts in the sort of way that a person who believes in God should act. His/her behaviour is morally correct.

For physical training is of some value, but godliness has value for all things, holding promise for both the present life and the life to come.

1 Timothy 4:8

2) Look at the passage in which the word appears.

The term appears to be a comprehensive one in the setting (verses 7 and 8).

In verse 7, "training oneself for the purpose of godliness" is contrasted with "having to do with worldly fables fit only for old women".

In verse 8, "bodily discipline" is contrasted with "godliness" and by implication "training oneself for godliness". "Godliness" is profitable "for all things" since it holds promise both for the present and for the future, while bodily discipline (presumably) only holds promise for the present.

The statement of verse 8 appears to be the "trustworthy statement" to which verse 9 refers. It also appears to be the thing "for which we labour and strive" in verse 10, and the thing which is to be "prescribed and taught" in verse 11.

Although we are given no 'definition', the passage appears to put forward 'godliness' as an attitude of life which:

■ avoids peripheral issues
■ requires concerted discipline to attain

73

- comes out of our hope in God
- holds promise both for now and for life in the future
- is a central truth to be taught amongst God's people.

3) Look to see if the word is used elsewhere in the same document.

The term 'godliness' occurs a number of times in 1 Timothy (eg. 2:2; 3:16; 4:7,8; 6:3,5,6,11).

In 2:2 it is linked with living a tranquil and quiet life while maintaining a right attitude to governing authorities. Verse 3 indicates that this is the sort of life that is pleasing to God.

In chapter 6, 'godliness' is again contrasted with peripheral and divisive issues. Godliness is said to be essential to right doctrine. Right doctrine "conforms to godliness". Godliness is also an attitude which does not crave money but is contented. "Godliness with contentment is great gain" (and by implication, worth striving for).

1 Timothy 3:16* is a key passage in that it appears to give the source and definition of godliness. Paul talks about "the mystery of godliness". In the New Testament 'mystery' means a secret which has previously been hidden but is now revealed in Christ. Paul is saying that the acquisition of godliness is no longer a mystery and then proceeds to describe the life and ministry of Jesus from the incarnation to the ascension. The implication is that "the mystery of godliness" is revealed in the birth, life, death, resurrection, ascension and proclamation of Jesus. In simpler terms, if you want to know what godliness is, it is living a life focussed upon who Jesus is and what he has done.

4) Look at other writings by the same person.

Paul also uses the word in 2 Timothy 3:5 and Titus 1:1.

In 2 Timothy 3:5 he speaks of people who have "a form of godliness", but who deny its power.

Titus 1:1 speaks again of "the truth which is according to godliness".

5) Look at other people writing at the same time.

The New Bible Dictionary gives us some help, but not much, when it says, "*eusebeia* in pagan literature basically means the right respect due to men or gods, but in the Scriptures this word group (like *theosebeia*, found only in 1 Timothy 2:10) refers exclusively to reverence towards

> *Beyond all question, the mystery of godliness is great:*
> *He appeared in a body, was vindicated by the Spirit, was seen by angels, was preached among the nations, was believed on in the world, was taken up in glory.*
>
> *1 Timothy 3:16*

God (except 1 Timothy 5:4, where it means proper regard for one's own household)."

The New International Dictionary of New Testament Theology is more helpful. It says:

> Words deriving from the stem 'seb-' are very frequent in Greek, and convey the idea of devoutness and religiousness so characteristic of the Greeks. This devoutness does not consist—as in the Bible—in a committed obedience to a single, personally conceived God; but rather in a holy trepidation, wonder, or admiration called forth by a majesty in things, men or deities. Accordingly religious homage can be paid to very different objects: one's country, a landscape, dreams, parents, heroes, the dead, etc.

6) Look at other people writing at the same time, from similar backgrounds and under similar influences.

The word does appear elsewhere in the New Testament: Acts 3:12; 2 Peter 1:3,6,7; 3:11.

In Acts 3, 'godliness' has a slightly negative connotation. Peter is concerned that the onlookers might think that he is able to perform miracles by some extraordinary power or personal piety. For this reason, he makes clear that rather than being caused by some personal power or piety, it is through Jesus and faith in his name that the healing has occurred (verse 16).

In 2 Peter 1:3 godliness comes through "our knowledge of him who has called us by his own glory and goodness". In 1:6-7 it is one of the characteristics of a growing and productive Christian lifestyle. In 2 Peter 3:11*, 'godliness' is linked with holiness, which together make up the lifestyle of those waiting for the end.

7) Consider the writings/teachings of other people whose words or teaching have significantly influenced the author.

The Greek Old Testament rarely uses the word or its cognates. *The New International Dictionary of New Testament Theology* makes the point that this is probably because "the basis of Old Testament piety is quite different from that of Hellenism. God the creator lays claim on man's service in thought, word and deed; he requires active obedience, not devout trepidation to which lip-service is paid just on fixed occasions in cultic homage, or in the sphere of intellectual rhetoric. This active obedience, together with worship, is the characteristic feature of the fear of God, which is essentially the OT (as opposed to the Greek) idea of piety.'

Since everything will be destroyed in this way, what kind of people ought you to be? You ought to live holy and godly lives as you look forward to the day of God and speed its coming.

2 Peter 3:11-12

75

From this study you can see that in his later letters Paul was happy to use the word 'godliness' but only after he had redefined it. For Paul, the word represented the place where our relationship with God and our knowledge of Christ intersected with everyday living. Godliness is a comprehensive term for a lifestyle lived in the light of all that Jesus is and all that he has done.

With this background we can go back to 1 Timothy 4:8 and see if this fits the context and helps us understand exactly why "this is a trustworthy saying that deserves full acceptance".

Hands on

1

Go through your text of Haggai, writing down the words which
    a) you don't understand, and
    b) which appear to be significant.

List of words:

Where relevant, go through the seven suggested steps for discovering the meaning of the words you have noted down. Use a concordance, cross reference Bible and Bible Dictionary where necessary. (We have listed some of the important words below with space for summarizing your findings, as well as space at the end for any other words you want to chase up.)

Make sure that you read the following *New Bible Dictionary* articles: *Clean and Unclean; Day of the Lord; Glory; Ornaments* (which will lead you to the article on *Seal*); *Spirit, Holy Spirit* (first two sections); *Temple; Election; Servant of the Lord* (for 'Servant of the Lord', also look at a concordance—it will point you to passages like 2 Samuel 7:19, Psalm 89:3 and Zechariah 3:8 which are not mentioned in the NBD article).

You will notice that there is no NBD article on 'remnant'. Try finding out the background/meaning of the word by chasing cross references in other parts of the Old Testament. The same could apply for 'signet ring'.

NB. Your analysis of the structure of Haggai should have indicated the importance of 2:23. The words used here ('that day', 'servant', 'signet ring', 'chosen') are theologically packed and very significant. Understanding these words and their background is crucial for understanding the whole book.

Jot down a summary of your findings in the space provided.

'remnant' (1:12,14; 2:2)

'the house of the Lord'

'glory' (2:3,9)

'covenant' (2:5)

'spirit'

'defiled' (2:10-14)

'signet ring' (2:23)

'that day' (2:23)

Others you noted...

2

Work out the meaning of 'the peace of God' in Philippians 4:7.

■ Immediate context (Don't forget that 'peace of God' can mean either 'peace from God' or 'peace which belongs to God')

■ Context of the book (cf Philippians 1:2; 4:7,9)

■ Context of the writer (cf Romans 1:7; 2:10; 3:17; 5:1; 8:6;
14:17,19; 15:13,33; 16:20; 1 Corinthians 1:3; 7:15; 14:33;
16:11; 2 Corinthians 1:2; 13:11; Galatians 1:3; 5:22; 6:16;
Ephesians 1:2; 2:14,15,17; 4:3; 6:15,23; Colossians 1:2;
3:15; 1 Thessalonians 1:1; 5:3,23; 2 Thessalonians 1:2;
3:16; 1 Timothy 1:2; 2 Timothy 1:2; 2:22; Titus 1:4;
Philemon 3)

■ Context of the day. Read the following entry from *The
New International Dictionary of New Testament Theology.*

'peace' denotes in profane Greek the antithesis to war, or
the condition resulting from a cessation of war. Peace is the
state of law and order which gives rise to the blessings of
prosperity.

In Plato and Epictetus 'peace' can also denote peaceful
conduct, though peaceableness towards others is generally
rendered by *philia* (love, friendship) or *homonia* (unity, concord); and a peaceful frame of mind by *galene* (calm). Not
until the Stoics (Epictetus and Marcus Aurelius) does peace
occur in the sense of spiritual peace. But even so, the word
is not common in their writings, and *galene* is more frequent
in Marcus Aurelius.

■ Context of the Testament (Matthew 10:13,34; Mark 5:34; Luke 1:79; 2:14,29; 7:50; 8:48; 10:5,6; 12:51; 14:32; 19:38,42; 24:36; John 14:27; 16:33; 20:19,21,26; Acts 9:31; 10:36; 12:20; 15:33; 16:36; 24:2; Hebrews 7:2; 12:14; 13:20; 3:18; 1 Peter 1:2; 3:11; 5:14; 2 Peter 1:2; 3:14; 2 John 3; 3 John 14; Jude 2; Revelation 1:4; 6:4)

■ Context of the whole Bible. (Given that the references here are multiple, perhaps it might be best to rely on *The New Bible Dictionary* article that follows to summarize the information.)

Basically the Old Testament word for peace, *shalom* means 'completeness', 'soundness', 'well being'. It is used when one asks of or prays for the welfare of another (Genesis 43:27; Exodus 4:18; Judges 19:20), when one is in harmony or concord with another (Joshua 9:15; 1 Kings 5:12), when one seeks the good of a city or country (Psalm 122:6; Jeremiah 29:7). It may mean material prosperity (Psalm 73:3) or physical safety (Psalm 4:8). But also it may mean spiritual well being. Such peace is the associate of righteousness and truth, but not of wickedness (Psalm 85:10; Isaiah 48:18,22; 57:19-21).

Because of the world's chaos through man's sin, and because peace comes only as God's gift, the Messianic hope was of an age of peace (Isaiah 2:2-4; 11:1-9; Haggai 2:7-9) or the advent of the Prince of peace (Isaiah 9:6; cf Jeremiah 33:15f; Ezekiel 34:23ff; Micah 5:5; Zechariah 9:9f).

■ Conclusions

Step 2.5

Geography

I remember the last time it happened. I was driving north through the city without a map, avoiding the main roads and hopefully the traffic. Right here. Left there. A one way street and a couple of S bends negotiated.

I prided myself on my sense of direction. I could not admit defeat. Five minutes turned to twenty and even I had to admit defeat. I was completely lost.

I dived into the glove box, retrieved the street directory, looked for the nearest street sign and guessed at the suburb. As I found the street clearly marked on the map my whole mind did a 180 degree turn. Somehow I had crossed back across Parramatta Road and was facing south again.

Looking at a map can do the same for your study of the Bible. It can turn your mind around the right way. You can see where you are and where you are going. Reading a map can help you to understand your Bible.

The truth is that geography can be important for Biblical interpretation and that many parts of the Bible will remain closed to us unless we understand the fundamentals of the geography of the Ancient Near East, and Palestine in particular. Climate and geographical circumstances often influence the thought, language, and idiom of a writer, and leave an imprint upon his literary productions.

Louis Berkhof makes the point when he says:

> It is quite evident, and therefore needs no elaborate proof, that the expositor should be acquainted with the physical features of Palestine, its climate, topography, productions, etc. How can he explain the poet's statement that the "dew of Hermon descended on the mountains of Zion" (Psalm 133:3), unless he is familiar with the effect of Hermon's snow clad peak on the mists that are constantly arising from the ravines at its foot? How shall he interpret such expressions as "the glory of Lebanon" and "the excellency of Carmel and Sharon," if he has no knowledge of their luxuriant vegetation and surpassing beauty? What can he say in explanation of the use of chariots in the Northern kingdom (1 Kings 18:44ff; 22:29ff; 2 Kings 5:9ff; 9:16; 10:12,15), and their absence from the Southern kingdom? How can he account for the success of David in eluding Saul, though they came within speaking distance of each other, unless he understands the character of the country? Only familiarity with the seasons will enable him to interpret such passages as Song of Solomon 2:11, "For lo, the winter is past, the rain is over and gone"; and Matthew 24:20, "But pray that your flight be not in the winter."

(L Berkhof, *Principles of Biblical Interpretation*, p 121)

There are three important geographical areas in the Bible. The first, the Fertile Crescent, is important because it is from here that Abraham first came. It is also the source of repeated threats to Israel. The second, Egypt, is important because it is the place in which the most formative event in Israel's history took place—the Exodus. The third is Palestine itself, the centre stage of the story of the Bible.

A book well worth purchasing as an aid to understanding the geography of the Bible as it is linked with the principal people, places and events is Simon Jenkin's *Bible Mapbook* (Lion, 1985).

The Fertile Crescent (Map 1)

A line drawn from Ur through Haran and then down the Syrian coast as far as Egypt traces out a crescent. The narrow strip around this line is called the Fertile Crescent. This strip is rich in water and is therefore the centre of farming and the path which trade routes follow. For the same reasons it is also the route along which armies travel to wage war.

Egypt

The Jews find their identity as God's people in a series of events closely connected with the land of Egypt and the area between Egypt and Palestine. It was here that the Exodus took place, and it was also to here that the last remnants of the southern kingdom retreated in 587 BC.

Map 1: The Fertile Crescent

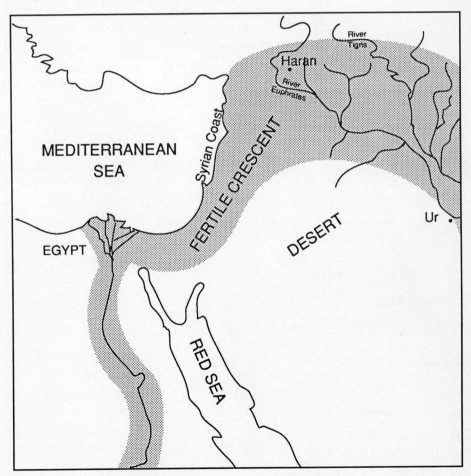

Map 2: Palestine
(showing major Old and New Testament locations)

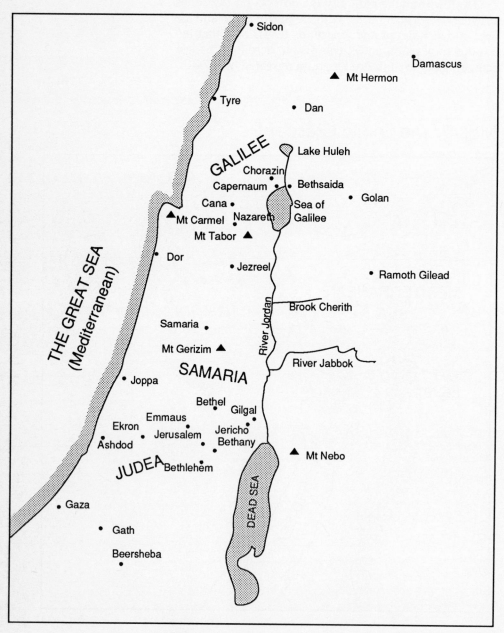

Palestine (Maps 2–3)

The centre of activity as far as Israel and Biblical history is concerned is the piece of land which we know as Palestine. Compared with Australia, Palestine is tiny. It is a narrow piece of land some 300-400 km long (if we include the desert regions in the south), and anything from 50-80 km wide.

The area has been traditionally divided into four geographical subdivisions running from north to south. Each of these strips of land becomes higher the further north you travel, and drier and less able to be cultivated the further south you travel. From west to east these strips are knows as: the Coastal Plain, the Western Hills, the Rift Valley and the Eastern Hills.

The Coastal Plain

The Coastal Plain extends for some 200 km from Gaza and the desert (Negev) in the south, to the borders of Lebanon. It is interrupted by Mount Carmel (the battle-field of Elijah and the prophets of Baal in 1 Kings 18). The plain of Asher to the north played no major role in Israelite history. The same cannot be said for the plain of Jezreel, a tract of land 50 km long and 20 km wide. This valley formed the main route from Egypt to Damascus in the north and so was the site of many strategic battles (eg. 1 Samuel 29:1). It is also the scene of the last great battle of history, the battle of Armageddon (literally='the mountain of Megiddo'—Revelation 16:16).

To the south of Carmel lies the plain of Dor and the plain of Sharon. The latter was the home of the Philistines (from which the name 'Palestine' is drawn) with their five major cities of Ekron, Ashdod, Ashkelon, Gath and Gaza. Further south, the plain is separated from the mountains by the hill lands of the Shephelah. This 'hill country', which formed a buffer between Israel and Philistia, forms the setting for much of the book of Joshua, various Judges and the life of David.

The Western Hills

The Western Hills are the Central Highlands of Palestine. They stretch some 300 km from northern Galilee to the Sinai. In Lebanon to the north, famous for its cedars, this range rises to over 1800 m above sea level. The highest peak in Palestine is in the north, Jebal Jermap (1208 m). Lower Galilee consists of a number of east-to-west ridges, none of which rises above 600 m. This area, hardly mentioned in the Old Testament, becomes the centre of attention in much of the New Testament, especially the Gospels. These mountains are broken by the plains of Jezreel and Megiddo which form an easy passage from north to south.

The centre of this strip takes in the important towns of Shechem, Shiloh, Bethel and Samaria. Together with other fertile basins, Samaria was exposed to outside influences and was easily enticed away from faithful allegiance to God.

Further south, Samaria merges into Judea, studded by the familiar cities of Jerusalem, Bethlehem and Hebron. In light of the history of Israel, it is interesting to note that Samaria was fairly accessible, whereas Judea was more isolated from outside contact. The slopes were steeper and more difficult to traverse, and there was little reason to cross them since the passage east is blocked by the Dead Sea.

The Rift Valley

The Rift Valley cuts a deep hole right through the centre of Palestine, starting at the foothills of Mt Hermon. This mountain, whose snow-capped peaks provide the source of the Jordan (Deuteronomy 3:9; 4:48), is not far from the town of Dan, which was considered the uppermost extent of Israelite territory. The Jordan, which flows all year, cuts through the Lake of Tiberias (or Sea of Galilee) some 200 m below sea level. This lake, with its

Map 3: Topographical Cross-section of Palestine

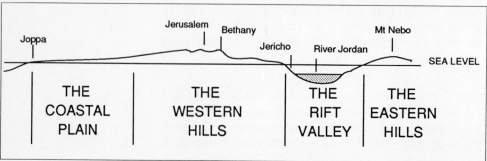

cities of Chorazin, Capernaum and Bethsaida was the main site for much of Jesus' early ministry.

From here the river, fed by intermittent rivers, winds through a narrow flood plain covered with thick scrub (the 'jungle' of Jeremiah 17:6) to the Dead Sea (391 m below sea level). This sea is known as 'Dead' because the only water which leaves there leaves by evaporation, thus leaving an accumulation of minerals behind. The Rift Valley continues south through the desert of the Arabah.

The Eastern Hills

The Eastern Hills, also known as the Transjordan, are cut by four important rivers—the Yarmuk, Jabbok, Arnon and Zered. They receive considerable rain and are fertile. However, the further east one travels, the less rain there is, and before long the fertile land turns to desert. The fertile strip reaches its widest point in Bashan, known today as the Golan Heights. Across this part runs a road from Damascus to Lake Galilee, providing an important route into or out of Palestine. Further South, we find Gilead and then the plateau which was the home of the Ammonites and Moabites.

Examples

Revelation 3:14-22

The following is an excerpt from *The New Bible Dictionary* article on 'Laodicea'. Read the excerpt and then look at Revelation 3:14-22. As you will see, the impact of this passage is only apparent when you know a bit about the city of Laodicea. This knowledge of how the message would have struck the original recipients in turn helps us in applying the passage to ourselves.

It lay in the fertile valley of Lycus...close to Hierapolis and Colossae...It was a very important crossroad...

This strategic position made Laodicea an extremely prosperous commercial centre, especially under Roman rule. When destroyed by a disastrous earthquake in AD 60 it could afford to dispense with aid from Nero. It was an important centre of banking and exchange. Its distinctive products included garments of glossy black wool, and it was a medical centre noted for ophthalmology. The site had one disadvantage: being determined by the road system, it lacked a sufficient and permanent supply of good water. Water was piped to the city from hot springs some distance south, and probably arrived lukewarm. The deposits still encrusting the remains testify to its warmth.

Daniel 1

In verse 2 of Daniel 1, the RSV records that Nebuchadnezzar deposited the vessels which he had taken from the temple in Jerusalem in the temple of his own God "in the land of Shinar" (unfortunately this is relegated to a footnote in the NIV translation).

The 'land of Shinar' is a strange and ancient way of speaking and yet it is quite deliberately used by the author. This can be seen by looking at its other occurrences in the Bible. A concordance will reveal that the 'land of Shinar' is the same place in which men built the tower of Babel in Genesis 11. This tower of Babel represents the kingdom of man at its height in the Bible. It represents man setting himself against God and almost defying God.

By referring to the 'land of Shinar' in Daniel 1, the author wants us to remember Genesis 11 and to pose the questions that were posed then. With the vessels of the Jerusalem temple now lodged in the temple of Babylon's man-made gods, we see a repeat of Genesis 11. What will God do this time? Will he repeat Babel? Can he win again? These are the questions that the author wants to raise in our minds.

These seemingly insignificant words (plus some other phrases in the first few verses) set the agenda for the whole book. The conflict is on. The greatest of the kingdoms of men is pitted against the defeated kingdom of God.

The original readers, familiar with Genesis 11, would have picked this up. If we keep our eyes on the geographical setting of Scripture we will learn to pick up such things also.

Hands on

1

Put together a description of the city of Ephesus and its people from the following sources: the book of Acts, Paul's Epistle to the Ephesians, *The New Bible Dictionary* article on 'Ephesus'.

2

What are the major cities of the following nations:

Assyria _____

Egypt _____

Persia _____

Syria _____

Philistia _____

Edom _____

Ammon _____

Babylon _____

Roman Palestine _____

91

3

Fill in the following map of the journey of the Israelites as
recorded in Deuteronomy 1:1-4:49, indicating significant
incidents and nations that were encountered on the way.

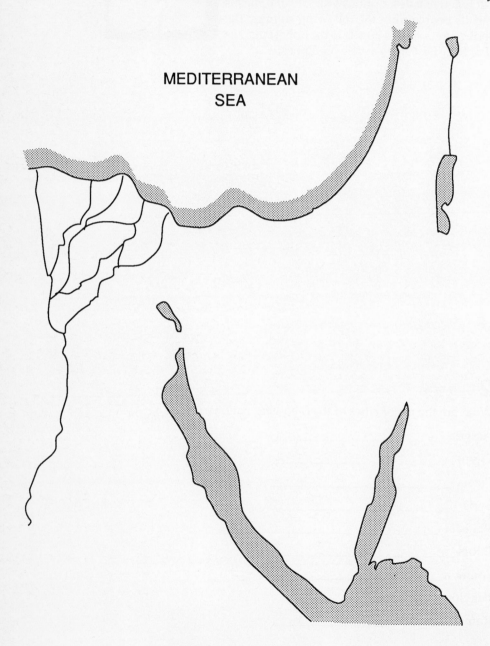

MEDITERRANEAN
SEA

Step 2.6

History

In retrospect, I suppose his reaction was justified. Nevertheless I was angry. I was not a thief, nor an addict, nor a forger. I thought of myself as an upright member of society, not some druggie searching for a cheap replacement for my dependency.

Yet as I went over the events of the day it was understandable. After a heavy morning's work in the garden, my mother realized that it was almost too late to get to the chemist. I offered to go on her behalf, and being the weekend, I was free of the constraints of shoes and decent clothes. I didn't think twice about jumping into the car in the jeans I wore, pulling on the holey t-shirt that was normal, casual wear at home on Saturday morning.

Looking like something the cat dragged in, and smelling similarly, I strode into the chemist and handed over the prescription. Sanitized and bespectacled, he looked at the prescription, frowned, looked at me again, frowned, asked me to sit on a chair and walked behind the six foot partition. He climbed its raised platform so that he could look down on me in non-verbal demonstration of supremacy.

Ten minutes passed. He disappeared behind another wall into some inner holy of holies only to reappear again, making directly for me. "Who is this?" he said pointing to the name on the prescription.

I explained that it was my mother.

"And what about this?" he accused, "Who is this doctor? Where is his practice?"

I'd only been to that particular doctor's surgery once before. I vaguely remembered that it was behind the shopping centre in a nearby suburb, and said so.

He disappeared into the holy of holies again.

Another five minutes passed. An assistant came over.

"There's no doctor of that name with a surgery in that suburb."

Getting angry at the amount of time being taken, I murmured some reply about it being up that way somewhere and suggested they try the same name at another nearby suburb.

And I waited. Being the son of two doctors, I was used to things medical and to handling prescriptions. I realized that something strange was going on. Firstly, it wasn't normal to grill people about prescriptions. Secondly, it wasn't normal to check up on the authenticity of the doctor who wrote the prescription. Thirdly, prescriptions shouldn't take this long to fill. But fourthly, a prescription for a drug on the 'Dangerous Drugs' list wasn't exactly a normal prescription, and I didn't quite look like the normal inhabitant of middle-class suburbia.

I also realized that the worried looks, hurried conversations and dialing of telephones could be nothing other than calls to the local police regarding a suspected false prescription.

Another five minutes passed. I entertained myself by waiting for the police, watching pharmacists and their assistants looking at me, and by getting alternately amused and angry.

Finally the attendant wandered over, abused me for not telling her that my mother was a doctor, and sold me the drugs.

On leaving the shop I saw two large, uniformed men emerge from the doors of a police van and come running up the street toward me and into the chemist.

As I reflected on it, the mistake was justified and the action taken, right. The chemist didn't know anything about me. He knew nothing of my personal background, my present situation, nor that of my mother. He only had half the story and he had no choice but to act on it. If he had known the whole story perhaps the mistake would not have happened.

We often make the mistake of the chemist when we

read the Bible. With a little more knowledge of the history of the author, his readers, and their world, perhaps we wouldn't make mistakes or jump to hasty conclusions. History is very important to the Bible. The Scriptures must be interpreted in the light of those historical circumstances that put their stamp on them.

Some Basic Assumptions

There are some basic assumptions that need to be acknowledged as we interpret the Bible:

■ The Word of God originated in an historical setting, and therefore can only be fully understood in the light of that history.

■ It will be difficult to understand an author and to interpret his words correctly unless he is seen against the proper historical background.

■ The place, time and circumstances of an author and the prevailing view of the world will naturally colour his writings.

These assumptions have implications for us, as readers in the twentieth century. We are going to have to:

➡ get to know the author, finding out as much about him as possible. Where is he as he writes? What things have influenced his life? What things influence him now? What is he like as a person? What was his purpose in writing? Are there any special circumstances behind the writing of this book/letter?

➡ get to know the readers, finding out as much about them as possible. Where are they as they receive this letter? Why are they there? What has influenced them in the past or is influencing them at present?

➡ get to know the historical circumstances. What political powers are there? What is the national history of the readers? What religious institutions are there?

❛ With a little more knowledge of the history of the author, his readers, and their world, perhaps we wouldn't make mistakes or jump to hasty conclusions.

The Author

The first question to ask of any piece of literature is: Who is the author?

Some of the books of the Bible let us know; some don't. But even knowing the name is not enough. We need to be acquainted with the person behind the name.

The best way to do this is to become familiar with his writings, paying attention to personal touches and incidental remarks that bear on his character and life.

NB. We should probably include a further section here called 'Who is the speaker?' The Bible often records the words of people other than the writer and it is important to recognize this and distinguish between them. Most instances are easy to pick up (eg. in narrative); others are not so easy (eg. John 3:16-21; Galatians 2). In the prophets it is quite common for the prophet to switch back and forth between the human author and divine speech. This transition can usually be picked up by noticing changes from the third to first persons (eg. from 'he' to 'I'). Sometimes the author quotes other people (eg. supposed opponents in Malachi 3:13-16; Romans 3:1-9; 1 Corinthians).

The Hearers

If we are to understand a particular piece of literature we need to know what it meant to the original hearers.

Becoming acquainted with the original hearers is especially important with the prophetic books and the New Testament letters. Almost all of these books were directed to very special circumstances and to particular needs. The author often took into account geographical, historical, social, industrial, political and commercial relations in framing his message. He often took advantage of his readers' moral and religious character, their personal idiosyncrasies, their prejudices and peculiar habits of thought. Knowing the original hearers often makes the difference between understanding or not understanding a particular passage.

> ' *Knowing the original hearers often makes the difference between understanding or not understanding a particular passage.*

When we looked at 'the author' we noted that there was sometimes a need to be aware of an extra category of 'speakers'. We should also look out for 'hearers' who are not the people to whom the literature is directed but people within the text who hear a particular person speak (eg. the Israelites listening to Moses).

The Contemporary Situation

There are some parts of the Bible that cannot be pinned down in terms of time or space. They are, in some sense, timeless.

However, most of the Bible is closely tied to an historical situation. The national history of Israel, its political institutions, its alliances, its relationships with other nations, and its kings and leaders, all play an important part in what the author is conveying to his readers.

The God of the Bible is the Lord of history. As the Lord of history, he comes to his people as they dwell in real historical situations and speaks to them there. If we are to understand what he is saying to them and how they are meant to react, we will need to acquaint ourselves with their situation and the various forces at work. For example, the words of Psalm 137—"Blessed is he who takes your children and smashes their heads against a rock"—will be difficult to understand unless we are acquainted with the people of Israel in Babylon, their circumstances there, and the factors that brought them there.

Practically Speaking

So what do we do? What sort of questions do we need to ask? Where can we get the information?

The Author

- Go back to the beginning of the book. Read it through again. As you do, note down everything the author tells you about himself.
  For example, note down his name, his job, his feelings, his credentials, his situation now, his biases, his attitudes to his hearers, the sort of allusions/illustrations he uses, and so on.
- Get out your concordance and see if he is referred to anywhere else in Scripture. But beware—if you find the same name, don't automatically assume that it is the same person!
- If your author has written anything else, have a go at reading it and ask yourself the same sorts of questions as above (about the author's character, situation, etc.).
- Ask yourself if any of the things you have found out about your author seem to have influenced what he is saying in the passage you are looking at.
- Check out his name in a Bible Dictionary. See what it has to say about him.

The Recipients

- Go back to the beginning of the book. Read it through yet again. Note down everything it tells you (either directly or by inference) about the recipients.

For example, ask yourself: What is their situation now? Are they involved in behaviour that needs correcting? Are they in need of rebuke, encouragement, praise, exhortation or teaching? Is their problem a moral or theological one? If there is a theological problem, has the teaching come from outside or inside the group of people? What does the author know of their situation? How did he come to know?

■ Think about the rest of the Bible. Do other parts of the Bible give you some important historical background to the people, relationships or situations addressed here?

■ Ask yourself about the relationship between the author and the recipients. Does the relationship have any impact on how they have received, are receiving, or will receive, the things he says?

■ Check out the recipients in a Bible Dictionary. What does it have to say about them?

The Contemporary Situation

■ Get out your concordance and find out anything you can about the people mentioned in the text, the political powers at the time, the religious institutions mentioned, and so on.

■ Look up relevant articles in a Bible dictionary or the introduction to a good commentary and repeat the exercise.

■ If you have the time and inclination (and a good library nearby), pursue some of these matters further from the bibliography provided at the end of the dictionary article.

Having done all this, try to reconstruct the specific historical situation that occasioned this section within the book you are reading.

> ❛ *The Bible itself is the principal resource for knowing the life and times of Biblical people.*

Aids for Studying the Historical Situation

The best resource you can bring to studying the historical situation of the Bible, is a good grasp of the whole Bible! The Bible itself is the principal resource for knowing the life and times of Biblical people. Get into the habit of reading large slabs of the Bible in an easy to read version (eg. NIV or GNB).

There are also a number of good, short histories of the Bible that are well worth reading. Get hold of one of these and get a bird's eye view of the flow of Biblical history.

A very helpful book on understanding the ancient world is John Thompson's *Handbook of Life in Bible Times* (IVP, 1986).

Examples

Hosea 2:2-23

Even the most cursory reading of the second chapter of Hosea will demonstrate the necessity of knowing information about the author, the recipients and the contemporary situation.

The Author

A quick read through the book and the article in *The New Bible Dictionary* will reveal the following information:

Hosea is the Son of Beeri (1:1), living during the reigns of Kings Uzziah, Jotham, Ahaz and Hezekiah (Southern Kingdom) and Jeroboam II (Northern Kingdom). We know little of his place of birth, job, age and calling, although the cities he mentions indicate that his ministry was carried out in the Northern Kingdom of Israel, although at times directed towards the Southern Kingdom.

The one personal detail that we do know a lot about is his marriage and family life. His wife was Gomer, the daughter of Diblaim (1:3). Gomer was a prostitute (1:2). There were two sons and one daughter born of the marriage, each given names that indicated God's judgement on Israel because of her apostasy with the god Baal.

Although not explicitly stated, it appears that Gomer left Hosea and became the legal wife of another man. It seems as though Hosea, under command from God, bought back Gomer from this other man (chapter 3).

There are indications that it was difficult for him to speak publicly in the Northern Kingdom, at least temporarily.

The Recipients and the Contemporary Situation

Although Hosea's prophecies have been preserved and were obviously read by later generations, they seem to be directed to his contemporaries in Israel. His ministry appears to cover the last thirty years of the Northern Kingdom, before the fall of Samaria in 722 BC. At this time Assyria was the dominant nation and posed a continual threat to Israel. Assyria was in fact paid tribute by both Syria and Israel as a way of staving off invasion.

At one point, Israel (in allegiance with Syria) attempted a revolt against Assyria, but this proved hopeless in face of Assyria's military superiority. The capital of Syria, Damascus, then fell to Assyria, and a part of the Northern Kingdom was annexed and its subjects captured.

Israel appealed to Egypt in an attempt to break free from Assyria. This proved abortive and the capital, Samaria, finally fell to the Assyrians.

This sort of national insecurity was the climate in which the book of Hosea was written. It was the final and most agitated phase of the northern nation's history.

Not only had Israel given up depending upon God for her political security, and turned instead to pagan nations, she had also adopted pagan gods, especially the fertility god, Baal. The NBD article on 'Baal' tells us that the Hebrew word 'baal' means 'master', which explains the play on words in 2:16. Israel had engaged in a sort of religious prostitution (cf. the similar ideas in Jeremiah 2 and 3). These two factors (dependence on pagan nations and pagan gods) were inextricably linked in Hosea's eyes. The recipients are presented as unbelieving, double-minded and fearful of their future. It is to this situation that Hosea speaks in chapter 2.

However, Hosea is aware of the history of God's people. In chapter 2, he proclaims that it is God's intention to bring back the 'good old days'. The NBD articles on 'Achor', a reading of Joshua 7, and going through the stories of the wilderness wanderings, will make the passage a lot clearer in this regard.

All this information is invaluable for understanding the passage. It is easily gathered by reading the book through a few times with pen and paper in hand, or by looking up the various Bible dictionary articles or commentary introductions. After a little while, looking up much of this information becomes unnecessary because you will have become familiar with the overall background. You will need to look up specialized information, but the overall picture will become second nature. Go back now and reread the passage. Is the general thrust of it any clearer?

Hands on

1

Find out what you can about Haggai.

Apart from the references in the book itself, his name occurs in Ezra 5:1 and 6:14.

We have no other information about him apart from these references.

The dates of his prophecies can be established with some precision. They start on the first day of the sixth month in the second year of King Darius (which according to the modern calendar is 29 August, 520 BC) and finish on the twenty-fourth day of the ninth month of the same year (ie. 18 December, 520 BC).

2

Who are the recipients of Haggai's prophecy and what was going on in the world at the time?

Find out what you can about these things by:
 reading Haggai again
- reading the first six chapters of the book of Ezra
- reading the background information supplied below, which is taken from Joyce Baldwin's commentary on *Haggai, Zechariah, Malachi* (IVP, 1972). You could also dip into the book of Zechariah.

101

The best part of a lifetime separated the deportation of 597 and the first return in 538 BC. The common feeling among the exiles was that they might as well be dead. Their bones were dried up and their hope was gone (Ezekiel 37:11). From a human stand-point they were right. It would have been hard to find any reasonable ground for hope, but to Ezekiel came a vision of res-urrection. God would re-create His people, reunite the two kingdoms under a Davidic head and set His sanctuary among them once and for all (Ezekiel 37). The encouragements of Isaiah chapters 40-48 laid new stress on election and covenant. The great Creator still counted Israel His servant and Jacob His chosen (41:8) and therefore they need not fear. He had blotted out their transgressions 'for His own sake' (43:25) and planned their return to Jerusalem to rebuild the Temple (44:28). Cyrus was designated as the anointed of the Lord to fulfil His purpose. Suddenly there was a glorious future ahead because they had an incomparable God who saw fit to forgive the past and plan redemption. The very heavens and earth would witness the declaration, 'The Lord loves him' (48:14).

... Jewish history began a new chapter in 539 BC when Cyrus, after twenty years of conquest, established himself as the king of a new world empire by entering Babylon as victor...

The next few years as they affected the Jews are recorded in Ezra 1:1-4:5. First of all Cyrus is quoted as saying that the Lord, the God of heaven, had charged him to build Him a house at Jerusalem (Ezra 1:2). The 'Cyrus Cylinder' sheds light on this statement, for the king records how, after his victorious entry into Babylon, he rebuilt temples and restored gods to their places... Thus the Jews were encouraged to return to Jerusalem to rebuild the Temple, and received back the sacred vessels which Nebuchadnezzar had confiscated when the city fell. After a long register of those who returned (Ezra 2) the setting up of the altar is recorded (Ezra 3:1-6). Sacrificial ritual was resumed amid the ruins of the Temple. Steps were also taken to obtain the official grant of timber allowed by Cyrus (Ezra 3:7), and in the second year a ceremony was held to give thanks for the inauguration of the rebuilding of the Temple (3:8-13).

Progress was short-lived, however. The people of mixed descent who had appropriated the land during the Exile wanted to identify themselves with the Jews by co-operating with them in their building projects... Zerubbabel and Joshua appear to have had the support of the expatriates in refusing to compro-mise with people whose easy-going religion and morals might encourage apostasy. The resulting hostility brought the work to a halt, and the Temple was still a ruin in 520 BC (Ezra 4:1-5).

Cyrus died in battle in 530 BC... His unusual liberality as a rule is well known... His son and successor, Cambyses, was by contrast a tyrant... Though the details are obscure it seems that Cambyses took his own life. In the absence of a direct successor

Darius, son of the governor of Susa and an officer in Cambyses' entourage, claimed the throne. Incidentally the march of Cambyses armies through Palestine, with the consequent looting and damage, may have contributed to the poverty referred to by Haggai (1:6,9; 2:16ff).

The death of Cambyses sparked of rebellions in many parts of the empire... There are differences of opinion as to how soon these rebellions were quelled, but it is likely that Darius had established himself on the throne by 520 BC, the year in which Haggai and Zechariah began to prophesy.

...The fact that the Persian Empire was in a tumult may have awakened memories of Amos's earthquake prophecies (8:8; 9:5). Judgment on the nations was beginning and prophetic hopes of a Davidic ruler were about to be fulfilled. If he was to come, the Temple must be ready to welcome him...

The right of the Jews to rebuild was challenged by the pro-Persian governors of Trans-Euphrates, who applied to Darius in writing for confirmation that Cyrus had authorized the project. An official memorandum was found at Ecbatana, whereupon Darius not only forbad interference with the work but also ordered material help to be given (Ezra 5:6-6:12)... the rebuilding of the Temple appears to have proceeded peacefully until its completion in 516 BC, and there is no evidence of official Persian opposition...

3

Find out about:
• Joshua, the son of Jehozadak

• Zerubbabel

• Zechariah.

4

Fill in the blanks in the time line of Israel's history below.

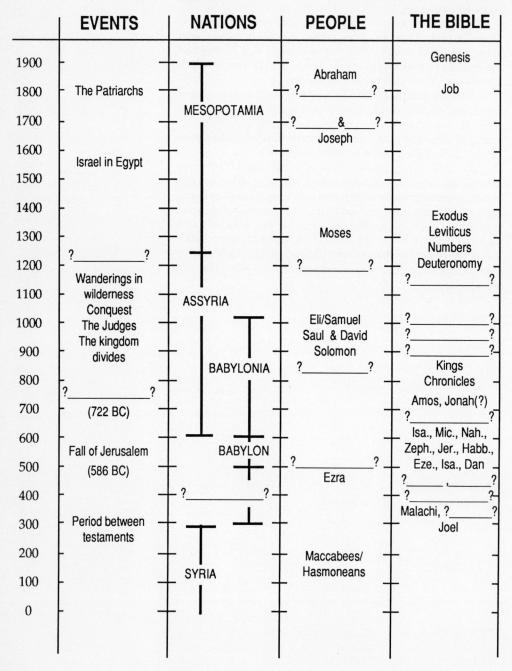

EVENTS	NATIONS	PEOPLE	THE BIBLE
1900			Genesis
1800 The Patriarchs	MESOPOTAMIA	Abraham ?_____?	Job
1700		?_____&_____?	
1600		Joseph	
1500 Israel in Egypt			
1400			Exodus
1300		Moses	Leviticus Numbers
1200 ?_____?		?_____?	Deuteronomy ?_____?
1100 Wanderings in wilderness	ASSYRIA		
1000 Conquest The Judges		Eli/Samuel Saul & David	?_____? ?_____?
900 The kingdom divides	BABYLONIA	Solomon ?_____?	?_____? Kings
800 ?_____?			Chronicles Amos, Jonah(?)
700 (722 BC)			?_____?
600 Fall of Jerusalem	BABYLON	?_____?	Isa., Mic., Nah., Zeph., Jer., Habb., Eze., Isa., Dan
500 (586 BC)		Ezra	?____,____?
400	?_____?		?_____? Malachi, ?____?
300 Period between testaments			Joel
200	SYRIA	Maccabees/ Hasmoneans	
100			
0			

Step 2.7

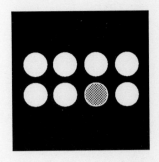

Context

...let us return to the metaphor of the skyscraper. Poems (and the same could be said of novels, short stories and even essays) are like elaborate, well-structured buildings: they have an overall unity composed of many substructures. But skyscrapers do not exist in isolation. The Sears building in Chicago does not rise up out of nowhere and exist in relation to nothing. Much shorter buildings surround it, and buildings almost as tall peer across the city-scape, slowly turning various shades of gray and brown and green. To understand the function of the Sears skyscraper, we must see not only its internal structure but its place in the city—one city, Chicago—in its relation to commerce, to the arts, to the on-going life of the city. And then we must see it as one dot in an even larger picture—the economy, the architecture, the life of the country. There is no end, this side of the stars, to the links this building has to life at large. It would be no exaggeration to say that in order to understand the Sears building we would have to understand the universe. And then, of course, we hasten to say, we can't do that.

James Sire, *The Joy of Reading*

Our studies started off with us reading the whole of a book—the big picture.

Before too long we then got into the nitty gritty of one particular passage within the book—the little picture.

Now its time to return to the big picture. We need to stand back and ask ourselves how this particular 'little picture' fits into the whole. In so doing, we are recognizing that the passage we are studying is part of a larger whole. We are recognizing that there is a danger of atomizing the book we are studying, of not seeing the forest for the trees.

We must aim to see how all the parts fit together as a single whole and how to relate the piece we are studying to what went before and what comes after.

There are two steps to this:
- Find the overarching 'purpose' of the book we are reading.
- Work out how each part serves that overarching purpose.

Establishing the purpose of a book

Sometimes this is easy, in that the author states his purpose explicitly (eg. Luke 1:1-4). However, most of the time, the author is not so obliging.

Either way, we will need to read the whole section or book again (the notes you made in Step 2.1 Getting Acquainted may help!). Ask yourself: Does the author explicitly state his purpose in writing? Does he imply a purpose? What are the special emphases or concerns that emerge? What words or ideas are frequently repeated? What, if anything, do these tell you about the purpose of the book?

When you are reading through the book, keep in mind that the author often gives away his purpose either explicitly or implicitly at the beginning or end of the book.

The question of context

There are two aspects of context that need to be looked at: literary context and ideological context.

Literary Context

Here we are trying to find out how the overall structure of the book fits together as a *literary* unit and how it flows.

We need to ask these sort of questions: Is the passage

self contained? What is the point of this passage? How does it fit with what came before and what comes after? How does it fit into the overall book? Why was it included at this particular place?

As you do this, pay particular attention to the use of conjunctions (eg. 'and', 'therefore', 'but', and so on).

Ideological Context

In this aspect, we are trying to find out how the overall *ideas* (as in idea-ology) fit together and flow.

As well as repeating some of the questions we asked about literary context, we need to ask: What is the point that the author is making in this passage? Why is this particular passage included in the whole? How does it serve the overall purpose of the author?

Up until now, most of our questions have been 'what' questions (eg. What genre? What meaning? What geographical/historical context?). Now we are asking the 'How?' and 'Why?' questions. Having done all this, the inevitable next step is to put it all together. This is the purpose of the final part of Step 2: Summing Up.

Examples

John 4:1-42

John 4 presents us with the peculiar story of Jesus' encounter with a woman who comes to a well in Samaria. The content of the story is as follows:

It is 12 o'clock. This is a strange time to draw water from the well in that everyone else draws theirs in the earlier part of the day. But at 12 o'clock, a woman comes to draw water. She is greeted by an unusual sight—a lone man seated at the well. The woman distrusts him, not only because he is there but because he is a man, and a Jewish one at that, while she is Samaritan.

Centuries have forged hate in her mind (and the minds of all her people) for the Jews. For their part, the Jews rubbished all Samaritan customs as being unclean, and Jewish men scorned Samaritan women as impure from birth.

With this background, the two meet in the scorching

sun. Jesus speaks and the woman is taken aback by his violation of all the proprieties of Jewish/Samaritan relationships. She retorts, "How is it that you, a Jew, asks a drink of me, a woman of Samaria?"

She is further surprised as he returns her hate with love. He promises gifts and challenges her. It is a twofold challenge. Firstly, Jesus challenges her to ask him for living water. Secondly, he challenges her to recognize who it is that is speaking to her.

However, the woman misunderstands on both counts. She thinks of the water as earthly water and of Jesus as less than Jacob. She is incredulous. Surely this stranger cannot be in his right mind to think that he is greater than the great forefather of her (and his!) race? It is impossible! If this is his claim, he is wrong. This woman and all her people had been content with Jacob's Well for centuries. How could this Jewish stranger produce anything better?

But Jesus does make the greater claim. He is more than Jacob. The woman has misunderstood him.

John 4 is not primarily giving guide-lines for how to talk to others about Jesus.

"Everyone who drinks from this water will be thirsty again, but whoever drinks the water I give him will never thirst. In fact, the water I give him will become in him a spring of water welling up to eternal life."

The woman is intrigued and then begins to understand. She begins to realize that Jesus is talking about something other than mere water and so she meets one part of the challenge—she asks for living water. But the other part remains unanswered—she has not yet recognized who Jesus is. Jesus takes another tack.

"Go, call your husband."

The woman backs off. No one likes being asked about their personal life, especially not this woman. She reacts instinctively, ambiguously, and perhaps even deceptively.

"I have no husband!"

Jesus affirms what she says. He pin-points her sinfulness. She begins to realize that this is no ordinary man. He has some God-sent quality about him; something of the prophet. She begins to grope after who exactly he is—perhaps a prophet.

The step is a mammoth one for a Samaritan. Samaritans recognize no prophets after Moses. Samaritans regard Moses as the Messiah. But she has been exposed. Her skeletons are out of the closet and doing a jig in the city square. She is keen to change the subject. To do so, she does the appropriate thing if you have a religious person to make conversation with—she asks some spiritual questions.

"Our fathers worshipped on this mountain, but you Jews claim that the place where we must worship is in Jerusalem."

Her questions are answered but Jesus refuses to be drawn into the question of where people ought to worship. Instead, he uses the question as an opportunity to speak about the essential nature of God, to speak about the kind of worship that ought to be offered to God. Again she is impressed. These are not the answers of an ordinary religious man. She cautiously sounds him out.

"I know that Messiah (called Christ) is coming. When he comes, he will explain everything to us."

Jesus affirms it again.

"I who speak to you am he."

She becomes excited, running off and leaving her water pot behind. The discovery is shared. And the second part of the challenge has been fulfilled—she has recognized who Jesus is, and as a result many others believe in who Jesus is—the Saviour of the world.

The story is straightforward enough. It is a story of a woman caught in a struggle to rise from the things of this world to belief in Jesus. This is the message of the passage.

Any cursory reading of the gospel of John will show masses of similar incidents. They all have the same thrust because that is how they are designed. John tells us as much in 20:31—

"These things are written that you may believe that Jesus is the Christ, the Son of God, and that by believing you may have life in his name."

John 4 is not primarily giving guide-lines for how to talk to others about Jesus. It is not showing us how we might change the topic from water to living water, from ordinary conversation to God-centred conversation. This passage is about an adulterous, unclean, Samaritan woman. And it is about how such adulterous, unclean Samaritans come to believe in a Jesus who is the Messiah, the Saviour of the world.

The irony is that while adulterous Samaritans believe, the rest of the book tells us that God's chosen people, the Jews, reject Jesus and ask for signs and wonders (cf. 1:10-13*).

A good knowledge of the purpose of the book as set out in John 20:31 and 1:10-13 will make this passage live.

He was in the world, and though the world was made through him, the world did not recognize him. He came to that which was his own, but his own did not receive him. Yet to all who received him, to those who believed in his name, he gave the right to become children of God—children born not of natural descent, nor of human decision or a husband's will, but born of God.

John 1:10-13

It is designed to contrast starkly with what has come before. In chapter 3 we see one of God's own people, a 'teacher of Israel', dismiss Jesus as no more than a teacher. Here, in chapter 4, we see one of the most despised races on earth accept Jesus for what he really is—the Messiah.

If we have rightly analyzed what the passage is about, we will be able to apply it rightly. We will ask ourselves: Who is Jesus? and What is my reaction to him? These are far more important questions than whether we are evangelizing the way Jesus did. What is more, these are the questions that the author wants us to ask. His concern is 'What do you think about Jesus?'. Answering this question will turn adulterers into saints.

Isaiah 40:28-31

"Have you not known? Have you not heard?
The Lord is the everlasting God,
the Creator of the ends of the earth.
He does not faint or grow weary,
his understanding is unsearchable.
He gives power to the faint,
and to him who has no might he increases strength.
Even youths shall faint and be weary,
and young men shall fall exhausted;
but they who wait for the Lord shall renew their
    strength,
they shall mount up with wings like eagles,
they shall run and not be weary,
they shall walk and not faint."

For all of us, these verses were well known before they found their way into *Chariots of Fire* at the funeral service of Eric Liddell. They have been an encouragement to Christians throughout the ages. In fact, for many of us, any reference to Isaiah 40 is a reference to these verses.

However, a close look at Isaiah 40 in context will show us that, though they are important as an encouragement, the meaning of these words is more complicated than first appears.

A close look at Isaiah 40 will reveal the background of the Israelites being addressed. The Israelites had sinned time and time again and had rejected the prophets sent by God. God had warned that if they continued to reject him, he would send a pagan nation to destroy their land and take them away in exile. In 586/7 BC Nebuchadnezzar arrived to fulfil God's promises. He breached the city walls of Jerusalem, razed it to the ground and carted its inhabitants off to Babylon in exile. In Babylon, the faith of the Israelites was in tatters. They were disillusioned both with God and with his promises toward them. God seemed to have forgotten them. The catch cry of their complaint is recorded in 40:27—

"My way is hidden from the Lord, and my right is disregarded by my God."

In Isaiah 40:1-11, God comforts his people by saying that they are pardoned and that his promises remain ("the word of our God will stand forever"), even though they feel as though they have withered and died ("the grass withers and the flower fades").

In Isaiah 40:12-31, God answers the accusation put to him in verse 27. He says they are wrong on three counts:

■ Because he is the Creator and Lord of history (verses 12-17)

■ Because no one stops his plans or purposes—this means no nation, no prince or king, and no pagan god (v 18-26).

■ Because he is a God who doesn't back out of his commitments. He doesn't get tired or forgetful of his promises.

Instead of accusing God, Israel should trust him. They should hope in him and wait upon him. If they trust in God, then God gives his word that he will not let them down. He will rescue them and they will rise above it.

The context, then, gives the passage more meaning. It is primarily addressed to people who are under the impression that God cannot be trusted. It urges them to trust him and declares that God will fulfil his promises.

The thrust of this chapter, then, is that God is faithful to his promise. This chapter and chapter 55 (which addresses the same theme) form the beginning and end of a section in the book of Isaiah. Essential to this whole section is the fact that God is in control, even though Israel does not perceive it to be so. He has made promises. He has spoken his word to Israel. His word never returns empty without accomplishing what he sent it to accomplish (Isaiah 55). Israel shall go up from Babylon. They shall go out in joy and be led forth in peace; the mountains and the hills shall break forth before them (Isaiah 55:6-13).

> *God comforts his people by saying that they are pardoned and that his promises remain, even though they feel as though they have withered and died.*

Hands on

1

Why do you think the book of Haggai was written?

2

Read the following verses. What do they convey on their own? Now look them up in context. What do they convey when read in context?

May the Lord watch between you and me when we are away from each other.
Genesis 31:49

For with much wisdom comes much sorrow; the more knowledge, the more grief.
Ecclesiastes 1:18

Not by might, nor by power, but by my Spirit, says the Lord Almighty.
Zechariah 4:6b

Do not worry about what to say or how to say it. At that time you will be given what to say, for it will not be you speaking, but the Spirit of your Father speaking through you.
Matthew 10:19-20

For the letter kills, but the Spirit gives life.
2 Corinthians 3:6

Stop drinking only water, and use a little wine.
1 Timothy 5:23

3

What is the flow of theological ideas in Romans 1:1-3:31?

Step 2.8

Summing Up

I stood beside what remained of my mother's car and stared back down the road, past the swirl of black skid marks, towards the other vehicle. It was pushed into the rock face at the side of the road and even in the darkness I could make out two unconscious figures slumped over the dashboard. While my legs rushed towards them, the rest of me fled, not wanting to see, not wanting to face reality.

But reality had to be faced. I was guilty. I was responsible. I knew it; they knew it; and the policemen who took the report knew it, even as I lied to them. And as I faced this reality, I gradually began to ponder other things. I thought about the events that led to the accident. I pondered the way my life was heading. And, almost imperceptibly, my view of reality began to change. I began to re-order my view of the world and of myself in it. I reorganized my priorities. I determined that some previously important things to me were no longer important.

It was as though the impact of the accident had taken all the neat little files in my mind which represented my view of the world and had thrown them into the wind. As I scrambled to put them back, I realized that they could be put back differently and that I had been stupid to put them where I had in the first place. Six months later, my whole view of the world, of reality, of God and of myself was totally reorganized. Life could never be the same again.

In his book *The Joy of Reading*, James Sire takes up an idea put forward by Alvin Toffler that "Every person carries in his head a mental model of the world—a subjective representation of external reality" and likens this mental model to a giant filing cabinet filled with files in which we can file all the information that comes our way.

He says that the major files in this filing cabinet include the following basic concepts:

- our concept of the most real thing in existence (our notion of God or of ultimate reality)
- our view of the essential nature of the external world (ordered or chaotic, material or spiritual)
- our idea of who we and others really are (our concept of human nature); this includes our idea of how we know things (epistemology) and our notion of 'the good' (ethics)
- our understanding of the meaning of humanity's sojourn on earth (the meaning of history).

Recognizing that we all have a view of the world and of reality is very helpful to us in Biblical interpretation. It helps us understand ourselves and it helps us grasp what is going on in the Scriptures.

Our World View

Each of us comes to the Bible with our own presuppositions, world view, or 'mental model of the world'.

If we are Christians then we come to the Bible as people who have given our whole beings to God. Our desire in life is that we should "not be conformed to the world, but be transformed" (Romans 12:1-2). As Christians, we recognize that this happens through God changing the way we think. God transforms us through "the renewal of our minds, so that we may prove what is the will of God, what is good and acceptable and perfect".

When we read the Bible, then, we are doing some reprogramming. We are allowing the Bible to target our current ungodly ways of viewing reality and to change them so that they are more godly. We want God to change our ways of thinking, acting and feeling so that they are more in line with his will. We want *his* world view to be *our* world view—his wishes, our command.

116

God's View

As Christians, we also believe that the author is writing under the influence of the same God whose will we want to know and live by. We believe that, as he writes, he is not only conveying words but also a whole way of thinking about eternal truths. We hear some of these truths being said explicitly (eg. "You shall not commit murder"), while others are said implicitly (eg. the story of Joseph, in which we learn about God's sovereignty and man's responsibility even though the words are not mentioned).

James Sire might say that we are trying to find out God's 'world view', but we could equally well describe it as discerning 'the mind of God' or 'Biblical principles' behind the text of Scripture. Whatever we call it, the point is that when we read the Bible we are not only looking for what God says explicitly but how God views reality. If we discover this, then we will know how to please him in situations different from the ones covered by the Bible passage.

Imagine for a moment that you are the original hearers/readers of your passage. Two things are happening to you as you listen/read. On the one hand, God comes to you in your situation and speaks to you. He challenges you to re-examine all that you are thinking and feeling in light of who he is and what his will is. On the other hand, you come with your own presuppositions about what God should or shouldn't be doing. You may be bent on listening and obeying or on closing your ears and rebelling.

In other words, as we draw together the threads of the passage, we should ask ourselves: *If I was one of the original hearers*, how would this passage challenge or change my way of thinking, acting and feeling? What would it tell me about:
- God?
- the world?
- myself and other people?
- the situations which I face?

Notice the use of imagination here in interpreting the Bible. This section invites you to imagine yourself in their situation. Imagination can play a very constructive role in

> *We should ask ourselves:* If I was one of the original hearers, *how would this passage challenge or change my way of thinking, acting and feeling?*

117

interpreting the Bible, if used properly—that is, imagining the situation of the hearers on the grounds of some solid Biblical research and accurate information.

Examples

Daniel 3

In Daniel 3, we see all the factors we have looked at in this step in action.

The story is well known from Sunday School: Shadrach, Meshach and Abednego are in Babylon as Jews in exile. They have been appointed over the affairs of the province of Babylon. Nebuchadnezzar makes an image of gold in the plain of Dura and commands that all people are to fall down and worship the image when they hear the sound of certain musical instruments. Shadrach, Meshach and Abednego refuse and Nebuchadnezzar punishes them by throwing them into a furnace. They are miraculously unharmed due to the presence of 'a son of the gods'. Nebuchadnezzar then decrees that the God of the three men cannot be spoken against in his kingdom and promotes them to higher positions in the Babylonian public service.

There is no doubt that the original readers were Jews (although there is some doubt about the date the book was written and therefore their specific situation). There is also little doubt that they were facing some sort of persecution under foreign overlords. Every Jew found it difficult living in such situations because Jews were so noticeably different from everybody else. They didn't worship the multitude of gods that the rest of the world worshipped, and were therefore suspected, hated, and even labeled as 'atheists'. In a foreign court, a Jew was very vulnerable: he was always in danger of giving offence to his overlords and being taken advantage of by others.

Imagine for a moment that you are one of these young Jews. You are in exile and you know why you are there: your fathers disobeyed the commandments and rebelled against the true God. But above all, they shattered the first two of the ten commandments—they worshipped other

❜ In a foreign court, a Jew was very vulnerable: he was always in danger of giving offence to his overlords

gods and made images of them. These two commandments were the core of your Hebrew faith and you know that the history of the Jews was the history of their failure to keep these very commandments. And so you are facing the consequences of your fathers' sins. Away from your land, home and temple you are determined not to follow your fathers' example. You are determined to be loyal and obedient to your God and his commands. You will therefore keep these two commandments at any cost.

And then Nebuchadnezzar, the ruler of the known world, sets up his image. You have no choice. You must defy him.

We need to remember that the text would have been read aloud to its hearers. Read it aloud to yourself. What do you notice? The author takes great delight in repeating the long lists of court officials in order of rank. He also repeats the list of musical instruments. We can only regard this as heavy satire. It's as if he is saying, "Take a look at this, will you. Here are all the so-called great ones of the empire. Look at them falling flat on their faces before a lifeless obelisk. Look at them playing an early version of musical chairs at the command of this petty tyrant!" He is sending up the whole charade, and appealing to his readers' sense of humour. He is saying, "It may be hard being a Jew in a foreign land but look at the alternative. Have you ever seen anything as stupid as polytheism? Have you ever seen anything as stupid as man-made religion? What would you do in their situation: die for reality or live as a fool playing the puppet before a transitory king such as Nebuchadnezzar?"

We have let the text transport us back into the situation of the original hearers. In the midst of their persecution, they would have laughed. They would have seen that it was impossible for any sensible person to do anything other than what Shadrach, Meshach and Abednego did.

The second thing we realize is that although an Israelite cannot commit himself to any alternative 'god', it is a costly choice. There is always, as in this situation, a cost involved in gaining and maintaining truth. A commitment to God and his kingdom will place you at odds with the kingdoms of this world. Serving the true God involves suffering, and there are no guarantees of being rescued (verse 17 is probably better translated "If the God whom we serve is able to save us...then he will. But if he doesn't ..." —so RSV margin, TEV and Jerusalem Bible).

> ' *What would you do in their situation: die for reality or live as a fool playing the puppet before a transitory king?*

119

The verse also conveys comfort. It tells us that God is with the Israelites, even as they suffer. It conveys to the readers the conviction that God will not prohibit suffering but will be with his people nevertheless.

Imagine, then, that you are the hearers. What would you have learnt? What would you be feeling?

Amidst your persecution, you would realize that paganism and polytheism are stupid and that the choice is really no choice. Like the three young men you must remain loyal to your God.

Secondly, you would realize that although there are no guarantees that God will rescue you, he is able to, and he will be with you, even if you cannot escape the consequences of your loyalty to him. You have learnt great things about God, about the way he deals with his people, and about the way you should react to paganism and suffering.

Thirdly, you have been encouraged to hold firm in your own situation and to laugh at the stupidity of the alternatives to belief in God and obedience to his commands. In a deadly situation you have been encouraged to see the humorous side of things.

Hands on

1

Analyse the 'world view' presented in the passages below, using the sorts of questions put forward by James Sire. (The questions are reproduced after each passage, with room for answers).

A

For everything there is a season, and a time for every matter under heaven:
>   a time to be born, and a time to die;
>   a time to plant, and a time to pluck up what is planted;
>   a time to kill, and a time to heal;
>   a time to break down, and a time to build up;
>   a time to weep, and a time to laugh;
>   a time to mourn, and a time to dance;
>   a time to cast away stones, and a time to gather stones
>   together;
>   a time to embrace, and a time to refrain from embracing;

a time to seek, and a time to lose;
a time to keep, and a time to cast away;
a time to rend, and a time to sew;
a time to keep silence, and a time to speak;
a time to love, and a time to hate;
a time for war, and a time for peace.
What gain has the worker from his toil?
I have seen the business that God has given to the sons of men to be busy with. He has made everything beautiful in its time; also he has put eternity into man's mind, yet so that he cannot find out what God has done from the beginning to the end. I know that there is nothing better for them than to be happy and enjoy themselves as long as they live; also that it is God's gift to man that everyone should eat and drink and take pleasure in all his toil. I know that whatever God does endures forever; nothing can be added to it, nor anything taken from it; God has made it so, in order that men should fear before him. That which is, already has been; and God seeks what has been driven away.

Ecclesiastes 3:1-15

What notion of God or ultimate reality is portrayed?

What view of the essential nature of the external world is put forward?

What is the author's concept of human nature, of how we know things, and of the nature of 'the good'?

What is the author's view of the meaning of history?

B

Old man
> You cannot see your way.

Gloucester
> I have no way, and therefore want no eyes;
> I stumbled when I saw. Full oft 'tis seen
> Our means secure us, and our mere defects
> Prove our commodities. O dear son Edgar,
> The food of thy abused father's wrath,
> Might I but live to see thee again in my touch
> I'd say I had eyes again!

Old man
> How now? Who's there?

Edgar (aside)
> O gods! Who is't can say 'I am the worst'?
> I am worse than e'er I was.

Old man
> 'Tis poor mad Tom.

Edgar (aside)
> And worse I may be yet. The worse is not
> So long as we can say 'This is the worst.'

Old man
> Fellow, where goest?

Gloucester
> Is it a beggarman?

Old man
> Madman and beggar too.

Gloucester
> He has some reason, else he would not beg.
> I' th' last night's storm I such a fellow saw,
> Which made me think a man a worm. My son
> Came then into my mind, and yet my mind
> Was then scarce friends with him. I have heard more since.
> As flies to wanton boys are we to th' gods;
> They kill us for their sport.

> > Shakespeare, *King Lear*

What notion of God or ultimate reality is portrayed?

What view of the essential nature of the external world is put forward?

What is the author's concept of human nature, of how we know things, and of the nature of 'the good'?

What is the author's view of the meaning of history?

C

Now when I say 'I', it seems so hollow to me. I can no longer manage to feel myself, I am so forgotten. The only real thing left in me is some existence which can feel itself existing. I give a long, voluptuous yawn. Nobody. Antoine Roquetin exists for Nobody. That amuses. And exactly what is Antoine Roquetin? An abstraction. A pale little memory of myself wavers in my consciousness. Antoine Roquetin ... And suddenly the I pales, pales and finally goes out.

Lucid, motionless, empty, the consciousness is situated between the walls; it perpetuates itself. Nobody inhabits it any more. A little while ago somebody said me, said my consciousness. Who? Outside there were talking streets, with familiar colours and smells. There remain anonymous walls, and anonymous consciousness. There is what there is: walls, and between the walls, a small living and impersonal transparency. The consciousness exists like a tree, like a blade of grass. It dozes, it feels bored. Little ephemeral existences populate it like birds in branches. Populate and disappear. Forgotten consciousness, forsaken between these walls, under the grey sky. And this is the meaning of its existence: it is that it is a consciousness of being superfluous. It dilutes itself, it scatters itself, it tries to lose itself on the brown wall, up the lamp post, or over there in the morning mist. But it never forgets itself. That is its lot.

Jean-Paul Satre, *Nausea* (Penguin, p 241)

What notion of God or ultimate reality is portrayed?

What view of the essential nature of the external world is put forward?

What is the author's concept of human nature, of how we know things, and of the nature of 'the good'?

What is the author's view of the meaning of history?

2

What sort of impact do you think the book of Haggai would have had on the original hearers? What do you think it would have taught them about God, the world, other people, and the situations that they were facing? What sorts of actions, feelings and responses do you think it was designed to evoke in them?

STEP 3:

Determine Other Meanings

Step 3.1

Links

Let your mind drift back to our *Overview*. Remember that there were two fundamental points about the Bible that we need to hold together:

- that the the Bible is the 'Word of God' with a divine author;
- that the the Bible is a human book, written by human beings in particular situations to other human beings in particular situations.

So far, we have spent most of our time looking at the 'human' side of the Bible (although I hope you've been remembering to pray for enlightenment as you've done so!). We have delved into the lives of the author, his readers, and their situations in order to understand what God was saying to *them*, on the basis that this is how God eventually reveals himself to *us*.

Now we need to turn more to the 'divine' nature of the Bible. You might remember that a number of implications sprang from our belief that the Bible was the 'Word of God':

- The Bible will have implications for us today
- We must stand under the Bible's authority
- We may well find that there are things in the text that the human author was unaware of, but that God intended should be said
- That the Bible 'hangs together'
- That the text of Scripture is primary

In Steps 3 and 4, we will deal with these implications in more depth.

How the Bible 'hangs together'

A few words of caution—when we look at how the Bible 'hangs together' and at the links between one part of the Bible and another, we need to tread very carefully.

Concentric Circles

First of all, we need to make sure that we work in *the right direction*. When we looked at the meaning of words (in Step 2.4), we saw that the best way to proceed was to work outwards in concentric circles. We placed the most weight on the most immediate context.

In looking for links between our passage and the rest of the Bible, we must work in the same manner. We must *start* with our passage (as we have done in the whole of Step 2). Then we can look at links between this passage and the rest of the book, then the author, then the Testament, then the Bible as a whole.

Links between parts of the Bible

We also need to know what sort of links we are looking for and how to find them.

In his book *Old Testament Theology: Basic Issues in the Current Debate* (Eerdmans, p 125ff), Gerhard Hasel helpfully suggests how we should forge links between the Old and New Testaments. His suggestions are also useful in working out links between any passage of Scripture and the rest of the Bible.

He suggests that the following relationships need to be kept in mind:

1) The continuous history of God's people and the picture of God's dealings with mankind

For example, Exodus 15 relates the Song of Moses as the Israelites rejoice in God's rescue of them from the Egyptians. This passage is linked to God's rescues in the past (eg. Noah) and in the future (eg. the crossing of the Jordan by Joshua, the rescue from exile in Babylon, and the rescue from the seven last plagues in Revelation 15).

2) The way one Scripture is quoted in another part of the Bible

For example, "out of Egypt I called my son" in Hosea 11:1 has direct links with the New Testament through its being quoted in Matthew 2:15. It also has strong links with history and the way God deals with his people referred to in (1).

3) The use of common theological key terms (eg. creation, judgment, grace)

For example, in Hebrews 2-6, key terms such as 'rest', 'sabbath', 'faith', 'judgment' and 'expiation' are mentioned. All are heavily reliant on the Old Testament use of these terms. All are pregnant with theological meaning that derives from that Old Testament background.

4) The use of major themes (eg. the kingship of God, people of God, exodus experience, election, covenant, judgment, salvation, bondage, redemption)

Even if the actual words are not used, one passage in the Bible may be linked with others through a vast network of major themes. For example, 'the kingdom of God' is mentioned time and time again in the ministry of Jesus. In fact, it can be said to be *the* way in which he talked about what God was doing in and through him. A concordance would reveal that the actual term occurs relatively infrequently both before and after the ministry of Jesus. However, the theme is evident from the first three chapters of the Bible through to the last three.

> *' Even if the actual words are not used, one passage in the Bible may be linked with others through a vast network of major themes.*

5) The fact of promise/prediction and its fulfilment

One of the things which distinguishes our God from pagan gods is that he "declares the things to come" (Isaiah 41:21ff; 42:9). He is a God who utters promises, who speaks words, and who can be relied upon to fulfil them. Thus, throughout the Bible, we see a constant thread of 'promise' or 'prediction' and its fulfilment. For example, when Daniel reflects on the 'seventy years' in Daniel 9 we should both look backwards to passages that promise judgment on Israel and a 70-year exile, and forwards to the New Testament where the fulfilment of the promise is seen in the ministry of Jesus.

6) The progress of God's saving history

As Christians, we believe that God has revealed himself in history—through events and their theological interpretation. This revelation of God is progressive. If we were to start at the beginning of the Bible and read to the end, we would see this 'salvation history' traced out in a series of significant events (ie. creation; fall; God's promise to Abraham; the exodus out of Egypt; the covenant given through Moses; the entry into the promised land; the Davidic monarchy; the exile; the restoration; the birth, death, resurrection and ascension of Christ; the consummation of the world). The pinnacle of this salvation history is the person and work of Christ.

> **' The pinnacle of this salvation history is the person and work of Christ.**

Thus, we should ask ourselves how each passage fits into God's overall plan for his world and into the supreme revelation of himself in Christ. For example, the blessing of Abraham in Genesis 12:1-3 can be seen as part of the continued cycle of sin and salvation in Genesis 1-11, and as a pattern and plan for the final salvation in Christ.

An excellent book on all this is by Graeme Goldsworthy, called *Gospel and Kingdom*.

Getting down to work

How do we put these ideas into practice?

We need to go through each of the six areas (just outlined) and sort out if there are any grounds for making links with other parts of the Bible. In other words, we need to ask ourselves:

1) How and where does this passage fit into the overall history of God's people?

This is done by looking at other parts of the Bible that address this particular period or incident, and by asking, "Where else in the Bible do similar events happen? Are there any links between this incident and others?"

2) Is this passage quoted directly elsewhere in the Bible?

If it is quoted elsewhere we need to ask, "Why is it quoted? How does the author understand or interpret it? Is the interpretation of it any different to the meaning it seems to have in its original context?"

A good cross reference Bible should quickly and easily put you onto direct quotations, as well as allusions in other parts of the Bible.

3) Given the work I have already done on key theological terms (in Step 2.4 Meaning), what weight should I put on their use in this passage and other passages in the Bible?

You have already done some work on what particular words mean and how they are used in the rest of Bible. Ask yourself if these words are significant in this passage. Do the links they have with other parts of the Bible shed light on the overall meaning?

4) Are any major Biblical themes touched on in this passage?
We should also be asking, "Are there any key Biblical themes which are *implied*? What theological background is presumed in the passage? Is there any development of the theme here? How does the theme develop throughout the Bible, and how does this passage fit into that development?"

5) Are there any promises given or fulfilled in this passage?
If there are promises given, we need to ascertain when they are fulfilled, how, and whether the fulfilment completely lives up to expectations. Further, we should look for multiple fulfilments.

If the passage refers back to a promise, we need to ascertain when the promise was given, and whether this passage is a fulfilment or merely a reminder or adaptation of the promise.

6) How does this passage fit into God's overall plan of salvation?
This is a fundamental question in Biblical interpretation. It involves working out whether or not this passage represents a new step or a regression in God's plan. We should especially ask how our knowledge of God's purpose in Jesus helps us understand this passage and its implications. Why do you think this passage is here? What was God's purpose in having it written?

Having got all this information, we now need to put it together. This is the purpose of our next step.

131

Examples

Psalm 2

In the following example we have applied the six questions to Psalm 2.

1) History

There are no historical references either before or during the psalm that help us fit it into the overall history of God's dealings with his people. The whole psalm, however, refers to the rule of God's king and therefore is most likely situated during the time in history when Israel had kings. Note that Luke considers the author to be David (Acts 4:24-26). This would place it during David's reign.

2) Quotation

Parts of the psalm are quoted or alluded to in other parts of the Bible. For example:

vv 1-2	in	Acts 4:25-26
v 7	in	Matthew 3:17 and parallels
		Acts 13:33
		Hebrews 1:5
		and others
v 9	in	Revelation 2:27

3) Key Terms

'Anointed One'

For background to the term, see 1 Samuel 9:16*. The term is the Hebrew word 'Messiah' which is equivalent to the Greek 'Christ'.

The New Bible Dictionary article on 'Anointing, Anointed' points out that

> Fundamentally the anointing was an act of God (1 Samuel 10:1), and the word 'anointed' was used metaphorically to mean the bestowal of divine favour (Psalms 23:5; 92:10) or appointment to a special place or function in the purpose of God (Psalm 105:15; Isaiah 45:1). Further, the anointing symbolized equipment for service, and is associated with the outpouring of the Spirit of God (1 Samuel 10:1,9; 16:13; Isaiah 61:1; Zechariah 4:1-14).

This article then suggests a further article, the one on 'Messiah', which gives an excellent and extensive survey

"About this time tomorrow I will send you a man from the land of Benjamin. Anoint him leader over my people Israel; he will deliver my people from the hand of the Philistines."

1 Samuel 9:16

of the term throughout the Bible. On the uses of 'anointed' in the psalms, the writer says,

> There are certain psalms which centre on the king, and they depict a very precise character and career. Summarizing, this king meets world-opposition (2:1-3; 110:1), but, as a victor (45:3-5; 89:22-23), and by the activity of Yahweh (2:6,8; 18:46-50; 21:1-13; 110:1-2), he establishes world-rule (2:8-12; 18:43-45; 45:17; 72:8-11; 89:25; 110:5-6), based on Zion (2:6) and marked by a primary concern for morality (45:4,6-7; 72:2-3,7; 101:1-8). His rule is everlasting (21:4; 45:6; 72:5); his kingdom is peaceful (72:7), prosperous (72:16) and undeviating in reverence for Yahweh (72:5). Pre-eminent among men (45:2,7), he is the friend of the poor and the enemy of the oppressor (72:2-4,12-14). Under him the righteous flourish (72:7). He is remembered forever (45:17), possesses an everlasting name (72:17) and is the object of unending thanks (72:15). In relation to Yahweh, he is the recipient of his everlasting blessing (45:2). He is the heir of David's covenant (89:28-37; 132:11-12) and of Melchizedek's priesthood (110:4). He belongs to Yahweh (89:18) and is devoted to him (21:1,7; 63:1-8,11). He is his son (2:7; 89:27), seated at his right hand (110:1) and is himself divine (45:6).
>
> ... We have here, therefore, either the most blatant flattery the world has ever heard, or else the expression of a great ideal.

Further information can be found in *The New Bible Dictionary* article, 'Jesus Christ, Titles of'.

'Zion'
See Exodus 15:17; 2 Sam 5:7. Other crucial psalms on the topic include Psalm 48. *The New Bible Dictionary* article on 'Jerusalem' (especially section V) gives a broader picture.

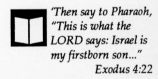

'Then say to Pharaoh, "This is what the LORD says: Israel is my firstborn son..."
Exodus 4:22

'Son of God'
Notice the background. Elsewhere, the term is used to refer to all Israel (as in Exodus 4:22), but especially the Davidic king (so here in Psalm 2 cf. 2 Samuel 7:14).

For further information you could look up *The New Bible Dictionary* article on 'Jesus Christ: Titles of'

4) Major Themes
The major theme of the passage is obviously the Kingship of God.

Genesis 1-3 (and the rest of the Old Testament) clearly

puts forward a picture of God as King; God as the one who reigns over the world.

Genesis 1:26-28 and Psalm 8 describe how man is made in God's image, and is given dominion over the earth. Man is to act as God's representative over God's world.

Later a shift in thinking occurred. God's rule was seen to be expressed not only through man in general, but through various figures raised up by God to exercise his rule (eg. the 'judges'). Later, when kingship became part of the structure of Israel, God's rule was seen to be exercised through his King or Messiah. Even later in the Bible, pagan kings (eg. Cyrus—Isaiah 45; Nebuchadnezzar—Jeremiah 27:5-7; Daniel 2:37-38) are spoken of in the language of Genesis 1 and Psalm 8 as exercising God's rule.

This later development was in part due to the fact that Israel's kings never lived up to their mandate (given through David in 2 Samuel 7). They failed to exercise God's rule over his world, as man in general had done.

Because of this failure, the prophets began to look forward to a time when a Messiah would arrive who *would* live up to expectations outlined in 2 Samuel 7 and Psalm 2. This idea grew during the period between the Testaments so that by the time Jesus arrived on the scene, the Jewish world was alive with expectation of a Davidic king who would fulfil Psalm 2 by driving out the Roman occupiers.

And a voice from heaven said, "This is my Son, whom I love; with him I am well pleased."
Matthew 3:17

5) Promise/Fulfilment

The Jews read Psalm 2 as a promise of a future Messiah (this was understandable, given that their translations put the psalm in the future tense).

The New Testament authors understood this as well. For example, Acts 4:25-28 sees Psalm 2:1-2 as a prediction of the conspiracy of Herod, Pilate, Rome and Israel against Jesus. Hebrews 1:5 and 5:5 use Psalm 2:7 to prove Christ's eternal sonship. 2 Peter 1:17 and Acts 13:33 are similar. All agree that the 'Son' of Psalm 2 is Jesus, not David, and that the primary reference of the psalm is forward looking, towards a Messiah who is to come.

Matthew 3:17* is particularly interesting in that it appears to be a combination of "this is my son" (from Psalm 2) and "in whom my soul delights" (of Isaiah 42:1). The combination is striking. God is saying that not only

134

is this one being baptized the 'son' of Psalm 2, but also the 'suffering servant' of Isaiah 40-55 (especially Isaiah 53). The kingship of Psalm 2 will be exercised through suffering.

In Revelation 12:5 and 19:15 it is Jesus who subdues the nations with a 'rod of iron'. On the other hand, we read in Revelation 2:26-27 that his people who conquer will also rule with a rod of iron, even as their master does.

(6) Salvation History

So how does all this fit into God's overall plan of salvation?

Perhaps we should view it as the writer of Hebrews does. In chapters 2-6 he uses a series of psalms (Psalms 2; 8; 95) to make the point that God subjected the world to man but that man has never lived up to his mandate. He says that we don't see man fulfilling Psalm 8 but that we *do* see Jesus, who is crowned with glory and honour (quoting Psalm 8) "because of the suffering of death". This Jesus is the Son referred to in Psalm 2 (see 5:5). His obedience, expressed through his suffering even to death, is the demonstration that he is rightly the king of the world. He is the one Man who has truly lived under God's rule and who, therefore, has every right to exercise the rule of God over the world (as expressed in Psalm 2). This is the one before whom we should tremble and whose feet we should kiss. This is the one in whom we should take refuge.

As you can see, in this last section on 'Salvation History', we have begun to move well and truly into the next step. We are starting to answer the question: 'How does this passage fit into the whole Bible?'

Hands on

1

Take out your much marked copy of the book of Haggai and your notes on it. Answer the six questions outlined in the study as far as the book of Haggai is concerned. Note that some of the questions may not be suitable for the book. In that case don't force it. The process is the same as for Psalm 2.

1) History

2) Quotation

3) Key Terms

4) Major Themes

5) Promise/Fulfilment

6) Salvation History

2

Research the term 'son of man' as used by Jesus. What Old Testament passages might have influenced his usage. Which Old Testament references do you think influenced him most? Why?

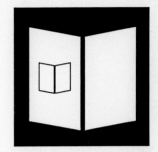

Biblical Context

When we come to the Bible, we come as Christians. As Christians, we believe in Christ and acknowledge that he is the Lord of all. We have pledged our allegiance to him and given our whole beings over to the worship of him. We have also come to see that he is the centre of all God's purposes—the Word of God *par excellence*.

Because we are believers in Jesus and in God's purposes revealed in him, we have certain convictions about the Bible. We are convinced that:

- the Bible is to be treated as a unity
- the Bible has a purpose
- the centre of God's purpose as revealed in the Bible is found in the person and work of Jesus.

Each of these convictions has implications for how we treat the Bible.

The Unity of the Bible

Christians understand that the Old Testament is incomplete. It waits for an end—it holds out a hope for the future.

On the other hand, Christians also understand that the New Testament is built on the Old Testament and is unintelligible without it.

Louis Berkhof, in his *Principles of Biblical Interpretation*, has summarized some of the implications this has for us as we read the Bible. He says that in the interpretation of the Old and New Testaments, we should be guided by the following considerations:

■ The Old Testament offers the key to the right interpretation of the New.

■ The New Testament is a commentary on the Old.

■ On the one hand, the interpreter should be aware of minimizing the Old Testament.

■ On the other hand, he should guard against reading too much into the Old Testament.

The Purpose of the Bible

Christians not only approach the Bible as a united whole, they also consider it to be a book with a *purpose*. This was how Paul urged Timothy to read the Bible. And it is how we should all read it.

> But as for you, continue in what you have learned and have become convinced of, because you know those from whom you learned it, and how from infancy you have known the holy Scriptures, which are able to make you wise for salvation through faith in Christ Jesus.
>
> 2 Timothy 3:14-15

As we read the Bible, we are to keep in mind the purpose for which it was written. It was written "to make us wise for salvation"—its purpose is salvation. In other words, the Bible aims to deliver humanity from evil and into fellowship with God. This purpose is carried out as the Bible tells us how God has been active in his world and what his acts mean.

Earlier in our method, we observed that every interpreter of the Bible needs to have a general grasp of history and geography to fully understand the Bible.

However, each Bible student should also aim to have an overall feel for the Bible in terms of its theology: what it reveals about God and his purpose and how that purpose unfolds. We need to ask: How does God reveal himself progressively to his people? What is the process of God's self revelation and plan of salvation as recorded in the Bible?

It is not difficult to construct a broad outline. God reveals himself firstly in his creation. His revelation reaches its climax in Jesus Christ and its conclusion in the consummation of the world when he sets up a new heaven and a new earth.

However, we need to fill in the gaps between these three cosmic points of revelation and make clear what such things tell us about God. This will give us a feel for how the whole Bible 'hangs together'.

But more than this, if we accept that the purpose of the Bible is to bring people to salvation, this will shape our interpretation. We will understand that separate books of the Bible are organically related to each other. They are united in what they think God is doing in his world and how he does it. We will ask ourselves how particular passages teach us about God's purpose of salvation and how they fit into that overall purpose.

The Centre of the Bible

We believe that the centre of both Testaments, and the link between them, is the person and work of Jesus. This was Jesus' own understanding and that of his followers (eg. John 5:39-40*; Luke 24:44- 47; Hebrews 1:1-4). When the authors of the New Testament look at the Old Testament, they see Jesus as the 'key' to understanding it (eg. Mark 12:1-11; Galatians 3:16).

The implication for us is plain—when we read the Scriptures, we must let them point us in the right direction. We must see that they teach us about God's purpose of salvation as revealed in the person and work of Jesus. They bear witness to him. We must receive that witness and come to him that we might have life.

However, it would be wrong to think that Jesus and the New Testament writers didn't allow the Old Testament to speak for itself. For example, Jesus urges the Pharisees to act mercifully on the grounds of the plain meaning of Micah 6:6-8 (see Matthew 9:13), and the New Testament authors told the children of Gentile parents that they should obey their parents just as the Old Testament urged them to (Ephesians 6:1-3).

Because we are Christians, we must interpret the Bible in the light of these two facts:
- the Bible as a whole must be seen for what it is—a witness to Jesus
- the Old Testament must be allowed to speak for itself; it must not always be read through the New Testament.

"You diligently study the Scriptures because you think that by them you possess eternal life. These are the Scriptures that testify about me, yet you refuse to come to me to have life."

John 5:39-40

141

Putting it All Together

When all this is put together, we should ask ourselves the following sorts of questions as we look at a passage of Scripture:

- What place does this passage play in the whole Bible?
- How does it fit into God's plan of salvation as displayed in Jesus?
- What does it add to what we already know about God and his purpose?
- How would the message of the Bible be less complete if this passage did not exist?
- How does this passage 'bear witness to Jesus'?
- How does it function as part of the whole Bible?

How about Other Christians?

When we study the Bible, we are not the only people doing so. Other Christians in all ages have studied the passages that we are studying, and have studied them in lesser or greater detail than we have.

These people, who have the same presuppositions as us and the same Spirit, can be of great assistance. We ought not to be embarrassed to compare our conclusions with theirs, and to see if they have reached different conclusions. We can do this by consulting their commentaries and other writings.

Examples

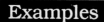

Proverbs 9

This parable presents us with two women calling out to young men in the market place. The first woman is Wisdom (9:1-6). Her call is away from simplicity and towards wisdom and insight (v 6) and thereby life (vv 11-12).

The second woman is Folly (9:13-18). She is an adulteress. She too calls men away from simplicity, but towards secret favours (v 17). The result of accepting her call is death (v 18).

Verses 7-12 are sandwiched between these two calls.

Verses 7-9 deal with a theme that is common to wisdom writers—the attitude one should take towards those who accept or reject the invitation of wisdom. The latter are beyond reform; there is no use throwing pearls before such swine. The teacher of wisdom should concentrate upon those who receive the invitation. He should give his time to those who welcome wisdom, to those who accept her invitation.

Verses 10-12 speak of the heart of wisdom. In verses 10-11, wisdom is clearly defined and its source is identified. True wisdom does not come via intellectual clarity or discrimination; nor does it come via astuteness of mind. Rather, it comes from religious commitment—the fear of the Lord. To be truly wise is to fear the Lord.

A quick read of *The New Bible Dictionary* articles on 'wisdom' and 'wisdom literature' will make clear that this 'fear of the Lord' is the foundation of all Hebrew 'wisdom' literature. Although other ancient nations knew of this sort of writing and thinking (they probably brought it to Israel), the writers of the Bible didn't merely accept it as it came to them. They transformed it. They made clear that there was a basic premise that lay behind all true 'wisdom'—namely, that the world which wisdom addresses is created by God.

Verse 12 expresses another characteristic of wisdom literature: it is intensely individualistic. Each person is presented with two invitations and each must hear and respond. When we do, we must also bear the responsibility and consequences of our choice. The choice is: If you are wise, your wisdom will reward you; if you are a mocker, you alone will suffer.

As we think about how this fits into the whole Bible, we can see great similarities in thinking. After all, the Bible continually presents stark contrasts in choices: one leading to life and the other to death. A few examples would be: the choice facing Adam and Eve in Genesis 1-3; the choice that Israel had as she stood on Mount Ebal and Mount Gerazim and shouted blessings and curses at each other (Deuteronomy 27:9ff); the choice facing Israel at Mount Carmel when Elijah challenged the prophets of Baal and called Israel to choose between God and Baal (1 Kings 18:16ff). It is also there in Psalm 1, as well as in the words of Christ about the two ways, one ending in life and the other in death (Matthew 7:13-14*).

In the New Testament however, the choice between

> *"Enter through the narrow gate. For wide is the gate and broad is the road that leads to destruction, and many enter through it. But small is the gate and narrow the road that leads to life, and few find it."*
> *Matthew 7:13-14*

143

life and death concerns the person of Jesus, who is identified with Wisdom (cf. 1 Corinthians 1:30; Colossians 2:2-3). It is as though the writers of the New Testament saw that in Christ and the message of the cross, the ancient call of Wisdom is paraded before the world once again: wisdom or folly, blessing or curse, life or death. Just as in Proverbs 9, one factor bridges the gap and makes the difference between life and death—'the fear of the Lord'. In the New Testament, the equivalent appears to be 'faith in Christ', meaning faith in who he is and what he has done. Choosing life means believing in Jesus.

Hands on

1

Take another look at the book of Haggai. What place does it have in the thought of the whole Bible?

2

Below are what some other Christians thought about the message of Haggai. Do you agree? Why/why not? Jot down your impressions after each extract.

A

Certainly Haggai is in continuity with the program of Ezekiel and with the general message of restoration that Ezekiel offered (Ezek. 40-48). But his prophecy is no mere return to pre-exilic nationalism, nor is it given over to petty or cultic concerns. If it were, prophecy would be in its demise. But, on the contrary, Haggai argues that from the small and disillusioned post-exilic community there will arise the eschatological people of God. God has not forgotten his promises delivered through Moses and David, and they will be honored by the ushering in of his kingdom.

W.J. Dumbrell, *The Faith of Israel*

B

Haggai was a man of one message. He represented the God whom he loved to call the Lord of hosts, the source of all power, the controller of armies, on earth and in heaven. It followed that His word had authority; the weather obeyed His commands (1:11); the whole universe was in His grasp and would one day be shaken by His hand (2:6,21).

This same God was consistent in His dealings with men. Though they disregarded Him, He never gave them up. When they failed to fulfil His will He made life hard for them so that they would seek Him (1:5). When they committed themselves to His service He took pleasure in the fact and was glorified (1:8). He changed men's attitudes (1:14) and by His Spirit abode among them (2:5). He would transform the work they did for Him, and cause the nations to supply gifts of gold and silver, all of which belonged to Him by right (2:8).

Haggai listed no catalogue of gross sins. The Jews who returned to Jerusalem appear to have been law-abiding at this time, restrained still by continuing memories of the exile. What was lacking was dissatisfaction with things as they were, and the consequent drive to initiate action. Resignation killed faith. The ruined skeleton of the Temple was like a dead body decaying in Jerusalem and making everything contaminated (2:10-14). How could the offence be removed? By a concerted effort to rebuild, which would be proof and pledge of a change of attitude from resignation to faith. Once priorities had been put right the presence of the Lord among them would be evident from the prosperity that would accompany both their building and their agriculture (2:9,19).

This assurance of the Lord's present salvation and future purpose pervades Haggai's message and marks him out as a genuine prophet. The bare walls of the present Temple he can see clothed with the silver and gold presented by the nations (2:7-9). Zerubbabel the Temple builder is the coming Davidic ruler, or at least his representative in the contemporary scene (2:21-23). God's universal kingdom, in which the warring nations find their peace in capitulating to Him (2:22; cf. 7-9), is the ultimate goal of history, but Haggai sees it beginning in his own time as personal and community affairs are submitted to God's rule. It is not just that everything will turn out right in the end, but that the unchanging God is working out His purposes now: "My Spirit abides among you; fear not" (2:5). Thus present

145

obedience sets God's people in line with fulfilment of His ultimate purpose, and His Spirit fills them with the conviction that they are experiencing in a small measure 'realized eschatology'.

Joyce Baldwin, *Haggai*, p 32f.

C

The value of the book is historical rather than religious. The prophecies may originally have been connected with the cultic rites of the New Year Festival, but they represent a sad decline from the ethical vigor and conviction of those of the pre-exilic prophets. Haggai's chief concern is the re-establishment of the cultus, the shell rather than the kernel. While it may be true that without the shell the kernel withers, there are lacking here the profound insights into the nature of worship which we find in Amos or Jeremiah. Haggai takes the superficial view that material prosperity is assured provided the mechanics of worship are guaranteed.

Yet on a long-term view it must be said that, without the temple and the Judaism which centered on it, the legacy of the great prophets would have been quickly dissipated, and Christianity would have had no foundations on which to build. Haggai deserves to be remembered for his contribution to this. Zerubbabel was not the Messiah, as Haggai imagined, and the messianic age when it came did not bring about the downfall of the Gentiles and the enrichment of the temple, as the prophet expected; but the hope and encouragement which Haggai's message brought to the dejected community of Judah at that time was, in the providence of God, a significant milestone in the *Praeparatio Evangelica*.

From a historical point of view the value of the book is, of course, that together with the book of Zechariah it forms a corrective to the inaccuracies of the Chronicler and sheds welcome light on the obscure period between the fall of Jerusalem and the achievements of Nehemiah.

'Haggai', W. Neil in *Interpreter's Dictionary of the Bible*

D

One question remained to be answered for the post-exilic Judeans: What about Zerubbabel? In the tenth century B.C., God promised David that there would never be lacking an heir to sit upon his throne (II Sam. 7:12-16). When the Davidic Jehoiachin was rejected by God and carried into Babylonian exile in the first deportation of 597 B.C. (Jer. 22:24-30; II Kings 24:10-17), it seemed as if this promise had come to nothing. Second Isaiah therefore preached that God's care for the Davidic house had been transferred to Israel as a whole (Isa. 55:3). But Jehoiachin was released from prison in Babylonia (II Kings 25:27-30), and Zerubbabel, his grandson, returned from Babylonia to Jerusalem after the 538 BC edict of Cyrus (Ezra 1:2-4; 6:2-5). Zerubbabel therefore was a walking question: What about Zerubbabel? Will God keep his promise to David? Will Zerubbabel resume the throne of David, and will Judah therefore be freed from her foreign overlords to become once again an independent nation?

Some interpretations maintain that Haggai here promises such independence and that Zerubbabel is then heard of no more because the Persians quickly removed him from power and put down the independence movement. But we have no evidence to support such a theory.

Haggai's vision of the future transcends the limits of such historical and political speculation. He speaks not of the overthrow of Persia but of the subjection of all nations to God—of the destruction of weapons of war and the establishment of universal peace. In short, Haggai speaks, as he spoke before (2:6-9), of the coming of the Kingdom of God "in that day". And Zerubbabel is addressed not as an individual but as the holder of the Davidic office.

God will keep his promise to David. God always keeps his promises. In a stunning reversal of the judgment on Jehoiachin, who is symbolized in Jeremiah 22:24 as God's signet ring, which he tore off his right hand and flung into exile, God will once again place that ring on his finger in the person of Zerubbabel, verse 23. God holds his Davidic king dear! The judgment on the house of David is over, as the judgment on the people of David has been reversed by God's mercy. When the Kingdom of God comes on earth, the Davidic ruler or "anointed"—(called the masiah in Hebrew, christos in Greek, Messiah in English)—will be God's chosen servant and regent over all the earth.

God always keeps his promises. And so, when the Kingdom of God began to come among us in the person of Jesus Christ (Mark 1:1,14,15), that One born of the house and lineage of David came as the descendant of Zerubbabel (Matt. 1:12; Luke 3:27) and as the beginning of the fulfillment of this word to Haggai the prophet. He introduced God's Kingdom which has

147

no end (Luke 1:32-33), which will overthrow every rule and authority and power (I Cor. 15:24-26) and which cannot be shaken or ever pass away (Heb. 12:28). The word of God spoken by Haggai the prophet began to find its fulfillment in Jesus Christ our Lord.

Elizabeth Achtemeier, Interpretation: Nahum—Malachi
(John Knox) pp 104-5

3

How do the following passages bear witness to Christ?

Genesis 12:1-3

Psalm 22

Song of Solomon

Philemon

STEP 4:

Determine the Significance for Me

Determine the Significance for Me

"But we are not going to have our wives dress like prostitutes," protested an elder in the Ngbaka church in northern Congo, as he replied to the suggestion made by the missionary that the women should be required to wear blouses to cover their breasts. The church leaders were unanimous in objecting to such a requirement, for in that part of Congo the well-dressed and fully-dressed African women were too often prostitutes, since they alone had the money to spend on attractive garments. Different peoples are in wide disagreement as to the amount or type of clothes required for modesty. Not long ago one of the chiefs in the Micronesian island of Yap forbade any woman coming into the town with a blouse. However, he insisted that all women would have to wear grass skirts reaching almost to their ankles. To the Yapese way of thinking, bare legs are a sign of immodesty, while the uncovered breasts are perfectly proper.

Eugene Nida, *Customs and Cultures: Anthropology of Christian Missions* (Harper and Row, 1954, p 1)

What would you do in this situation? What would God do? Which is the right way—to endorse the principle of 'modesty' and to accept bare breasts but covered legs; or to insist that our western understanding of modesty is correct?

The way ahead is to press for the timeless Biblical principle of *modesty*, even though it might express itself very differently in different situations. This is what Bible reading is all about: discovering how God would have us act in our situation.

And that's very difficult, isn't it? After all, there is an immense gap between us and the writers of the Bible. The gap is not only one of time. We are separated by culture, language, world view, customs and anthropology. And *they* cannot come to *us* with a message free of cultural baggage—we must travel back and do the 'cultural baggage stripping' ourselves. It's a sort of reverse missionary voyage.

This is what we have been doing so far in *Postcard from Palestine*. Although we haven't stopped being people of our own background, time and culture, we have tried to journey back in time to think and feel the way the original hearers did. We have travelled in a time machine to ancient Palestine, and stood in their shoes (or should that be 'sandals'?) and said to ourselves, "What was it like for them? How would they have received this message? How would it have changed the way they thought, acted and felt?"

Now it is time to step back into the time machine with those ideas, principles, newly-learnt attitudes and feelings and travel back to the twentieth century. It is time we asked ourselves: "Given *my* situation, how can I be most faithful to the message I have heard, in my time and place? How should I change the way I think, act and feel? What does God want me to do here and now?"

In other words, we have finally come to 'apply' what we have learnt.

The process of application flows on from what we have already done in Steps 1-3. Our understanding of the nature of the Bible and the way God reveals himself to us in the Scriptures will determine how we apply it to our own situation. In this final step we ask ourselves:

What does this passage tell *us* about:
- God?
- the world?

> *Now it is time to step back into the time machine with those ideas, principles, newly-learnt attitudes and feelings and travel back to the twentieth century.*

152

- ourselves and other people?
- the situations we face?

What feelings and/or actions should it evoke in my/ our particular situation?

Notice how these questions are almost identical to those we asked earlier (in Step 2.8 Summing Up). But there have been some changes since we put ourselves in the place of the original hearers.

It will be helpful for us to analyse what has changed and what is still the same.

Some things change

Firstly, we have the benefit of looking at what the *whole Bible* has to say on things mentioned in the passage (ie. Step 3). In other words, we have some added information. This is most marked where the original hearers were before Christ and the New Testament. What they knew in shadow we now know in reality (Col. 2:17*).

The second thing that has changed is our world and the situations that we face every day. We live in a very different world: they spoke in Hebrew, Aramaic or Greek, while we speak in English; they fought with spears, swords, bows and arrows, while we do so with nuclear weapons; they thought the world was flat, while we think it to be almost spherical; they faced Roman oppressors, while we reluctantly face nothing worse than the taxman or the university examiner.

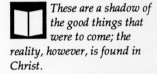

These are a shadow of the good things that were to come; the reality, however, is found in Christ.

Colossians 2:17

Some stay the same

For a start, God hasn't changed. He is still the same today, yesterday and forever. The things this passage teaches us about God will be similar to the things it taught the original hearers. Our picture may be fuller due to additional information, but the things we learn about our God are still the same, whether we live in the eighth century BC or the twentieth century AD.

Secondly, our culture, customs, language, technology and world view may be different, but there are some *crucial similarities* between us and the original hearers. We are still the creation of God. We are still inheritors and willing participants in Adam's fall—sinful human beings in constant rebellion against our creator. We still "suppress the truth of God in unrighteousness" and seek every way we can to justify ourselves before God.

In many ways, our world *is* like the world in which the original hearers lived. It is still corrupted by our sin and in a mess as a result. It is still "groaning as in the pains of childbirth", longing to be set free from its slavery to futility (see Romans 8:18f.). We still do not see man acting as he should and exercising the rule of God as he should.

The similarities are profound, and we need to be wary of magnifying the differences between us and the original hearers. On most occasions, the similarities between us and the original hearers are central and the differences peripheral. The original hearers of the Bible are very like us and we are very like them.

On one hand, when we put these similarities and differences together, we should realize that what God says today through the passage will be very much the same as it was for the original hearers. The answers here in Step 4 will often be the same as in Step 2.8. Because the answers are identical, it is inevitable that our actions and obedience will also be expressed very similarly. For example, as God tells us that he is the creator of the world who stands in judgment over his sinful creation, we, like the original hearers, should repent and call upon the name of Christ for salvation. Or again, as God tells us that we should submit to governing authorities, we will respect and honour our rulers, pay our taxes and obey where obedience is due, just as the original hearers did.

On the other hand, we need to realize that our situation is somewhat different to that of the original hearers and that our actions and feelings may be expressed differently. For example, as God tells us to be modest, we should rightly express that in a way that is meaningful in our own situation.

Examples

Daniel 3

Read our analysis of Daniel 3 in the 'Examples' section of Step 2.8 on page 116. How would things have changed since we last looked at the passage?

Firstly, our reflection on the chapter would have brought to mind some parallels in the ministry of Jesus.

Like Shadrach, Meshach and Abednego, Jesus held firm to God and his will. Like Shadrach, Meshach and Abednego, he was persecuted for it. Unlike Shadrach, Meshach and Abednego, he was not rescued from death, although he was raised from it three days later.

Jesus also clarified the principle that was evident in the young men's action. He said, "For whoever wants to save his life will lose it, but whoever loses his life for me will find it" (Luke 9:24). Losing your life because of your faith in God and allegiance to him is not losing your life—it is finding it.

And what about application to our own day?

Perhaps application of the passage could proceed along the following lines.

It is not easy to be a Christian working or studying in Australia. It is especially hard when you live and move with those who are not Christians and when they hold the upper hand. For Christians are, or at least should be, different. And they are noticed as being different. They openly reject many of the practices of those who surround them, and spend their time in weird sorts of ways. They insist on praying and persist in reading their Bibles, often in public. They respect authority and refuse to take revenge on those who are malicious towards them. They don't cheat in exams, or lie to the boss, and they keep to their word as far as getting work done. They don't think that the aim of life is pleasure. They don't follow normal sexual morality or get tied up with the excesses of their friends in other areas.

But more than that, the beliefs of Christians are very different. They believe in God and think that others should too. They are bigoted—they think that their God is the only true God. They believe that other religions have nothing to do with reality. God can only be known through Jesus, and the ancient Bible is the only definitive guide to how to please Him.

On all counts, Christians are odd people, somehow out of place in the modern world. It can be hard being a Christian in a pagan environment.

But then look at the alternatives. Look at the people you meet who live for their salary cheques, who bow and scrape in the vain hope of gaining advancement or prestige, who are at the beck and call of their transitory masters, committed to ambitions, careers, possessions, and their own little kingdoms.

> **❛** *On all counts, Christians are odd people, somehow out of place in the modern world.*

Or consider those who commit themselves, quite incredibly, to man-made thinking divorced from God—people who think that reality can be found in transitory human beings, or that utopia can be created on earth, or even that independent humans can find truth.

There is nothing so crazy or ridiculous as man-made religion, no matter what name it goes by. All man-made systems are exactly that. They will pass away as man himself will pass away. Death brings an end to them. Surely there is no choice. Will you commit yourself to the real God and to the reality that comes through Jesus, or will you live as a fool, thinking that reality is found in money, possessions, careers or the finiteness of your own mind?

However, opting for reality is costly. There is a cost to be paid in gaining and maintaining truth. Shadrach, Meshach and Abednego realized it. Jesus realized it and paid up. The disciples of Jesus realized it and followed their master. They knew that commitment to God and his kingdom places you at odds with the kingdoms of this world, and that service of God involves suffering. They knew that "everyone who wants to live a godly life in Christ Jesus will be persecuted" (see 2 Timothy 3:12). Reality comes with the cold, hard nails of a cross.

But if you realize this, you will know that in finding reality you will find life indeed. It will not be the transitory life that your peers are chasing but the sort of life that goes on forever in unequalled quality. The cost is worth paying.

If you have decided to pay the cost of following Jesus, then grasp the comfort that is given to us in this passage. The God who inspired this passage undertakes to be with you. He will remain firm to you. He will be with you in your deepest need and finally will vindicate you as he vindicated his Son, Jesus. What is more, the time will come when he will show up man for his stupidity, and reality will triumph.

Hands on

1

Take a final look at the book of Haggai. What is its significance for you in your situation? Work through the questions in this step.
What does this passage tell *us* about:
- God?

- the world?

- ourselves and other people?

- the situations we face?

What feelings and/or actions should it evoke in my/our particular situation?

2

Look at the following passages. What is different about the people and situations being faced? What is similar? What principles are there that are timeless?

Isaiah 40

Matthew 6:1-8

Acts 1:6-11

Galatians 2:1-21

James 2

3

Choose one of the following passages and prepare a short talk for your Bible study group that explains it and applies it to their situation? (Use your own paper)

Genesis 12:1-3; Exodus 3; 1 Samuel 2; Matthew 18:21-35; 1 Corinthians 1; Revelation 4 and 5

A Final Word

It seems like a long time ago that we talked about postcards and communication, but I hope that it is all making sense at last. As you have worked through this guide, you have learnt how to eavesdrop on God's *Postcard from Palestine* and glean the significance for your own life.

You have learnt how to travel in time and geography to another world, to hear God speak in that world, and to come back to your own world with answers for life. There is really only one thing left to say—put it to good use! Keep on using this method on other parts of the Bible. In time, you will dispense with working through the 'steps'. It will all become second nature to you—but keep using the method until it does.

If you're looking for suggestions as to what to study next, try some of these:

Genesis 1:1-12:3
Exodus 1-20
Psalms 1-5
Joel
Mark's Gospel
Galatians
1 Peter

May your eavesdropping change your life.

THE METHOD

Step 1: Depend on God for enlightenment

Pray that God would be at work as you study his word, enlightening you and moving you towards faith in Christ and a life of obedience.

Step 2: Determine the author's intention

2.1 GETTING ACQUAINTED
Read through the book that you have chosen to study several times, noting its overall themes, and devising a brief outline of the contents.

2.2 LITERARY TYPE
Find out what type of literature you are dealing with.

2.3 STRUCTURE
See if there are any indications of an order or structural pattern intended by the author.

2.4 MEANING
Find out what all the words mean in...
- their immediate context
- the context of the book
- the context of the writer
- the context of its day
- the context of its Testament
- the context of the whole Bible (if a New Testament passage).

2.5 GEOGRAPHY
Ascertain whether the geographical setting is of importance to the meaning of the passage.

2.6 HISTORY
Find out whether the historical context is of importance to the meaning of the passage.
Ask these questions:
The AUTHOR:
    Who is he?
    What is his personal history?
    What is his situation?

The READERS:
    Who are they?
    What is their history?
    What is their situation?
CONTEMPORARY HISTORY:
    Are there any other current events at the time of writing which have relevance to the interpretation of the passage?

2.7 CONTEXT
Work out what place this passage plays in the thought of the surrounding passages and in the book as a whole.

2.8 SUMMING UP
Draw together what you have learnt from the passage as you used steps 2.1-2.7. This should yield the significance of this passage for its intended audience. Ask these questions:
What did this passage tell the original hearers about:
- God?
- the world?
- themselves and other people?
- the situations that they faced?
What feelings and/or actions do you think it may have been designed to evoke in their particular situation?

Step 3: Determine other Meanings

3.1 LINKS
See if there are other passages in the Bible that have direct *word*, *historical*, *theme* or *thought* links with this passage...
- within the Author's writings
- within the Testament
- within the Whole Bible.

3.2 BIBLICAL CONTEXT
Determine what place this passage has in the thought of the whole Bible.

Step 4: Determine the Significance for me

Sum up what you have learnt from the passage in STEPS 2 and 3, thus indicating the significance of the passage for its twentieth century audience. Ask these questions:
What does this passage tell *us* about:
- God?
- the world?
- ourselves and other people?
- the situations we face?
What feelings and/or actions should it evoke in my/our particular situation?

Also available from St Matthias Press...

The Briefing

With a mix of theory and practice, warning and encouragement, *The Briefing* could be the periodical you've been looking for. You'll get 22 issues per year (twice a month) of short, sharp, thought-provoking material. Try our *5-for-5 Trial Offer:* 5 issues for the discount rate of $5.

2 Ways to Live

2WTL is well-known in Evangelical circles as a logical and accurate means of explaining the gospel. Now it's even better, with a completely rewritten training course and a fresh, contemporary appearance. New version of tract also available.

The Leadership Papers

Briefer and more accessible than a full-sized book, this workbook invites you to interact with the great themes of the Bible by researching key passages and answering 'Think it Through' questions. Ideal for individuals or small groups.

Fellow Workers

This set of discussion papers provides the stimulation, input and ideas that your Church Committee needs—whether you call it a parish council, committee of management, diaconate, body of elders, or whatever.

Investigating Christianity & Tough Questions

These two sets of evangelistic Bible studies are aimed at the enquirer, and are ideal for following up an evangelistic conversation or contact. They have both been recently revised and redesigned.

The Sydney Church of Christ: a critique

The teachings and methods of this new 'cult-like' group are causing problems for a growing number of Christians. This booklet offers a Biblical critique—a must for the pastor and for anyone who has had contact with this group.

Call us now on **(02) 663-1478**
or write to:
      St Matthias Press
      PO Box 225, Kingsford NSW 2032